Dimensions Math®
Workbook 5A

Authors and Reviewers

Jenny Kempe

Bill Jackson

Tricia Salerno

Allison Coates

Cassandra Turner

Singapore Math Inc.

Published by Singapore Math Inc.

19535 SW 129th Avenue
Tualatin, OR 97062
www.singaporemath.com

Dimensions Math® Workbook 5A
ISBN 978-1-947226-26-5

First published 2020
Reprinted 2020 (twice)

Printed in China

Acknowledgments

Editing by the Singapore Math Inc. team.
Design and illustration by Cameron Wray with Carli Fronius.

Contents

Chapter	Exercise	Page

Chapter	Exercise	Page

Chapter	Exercise	Page

This workbook includes **Basics**, **Practice**, **Challenge**, and **Check** sections to review and deepen math skills.

Chapter 1 Whole Numbers

Basics

1 (a) Write the number that is 1 more than 999,999 in numerals and in words.

(b) Write the number that is 1 more than 9,999,999 in numerals and in words.

(c) Write the number that is 1 more than 99,999,999 in numerals and in words.

2

Millions			Thousands			Ones		
Hundred Millions	Ten Millions	One Millions	Hundred Thousands	Ten Thousands	One Thousands	Hundreds	Tens	Ones
7	4	2	9	1	6	3	8	5

(a) Write the number in numerals and in words.

(b) The value of the digit 2 is 2 × ☐ = ☐

(c) The value of the digit 4 is 4 × ☐ = ☐

(d) The value of the digit 7 is 7 × ☐ = ☐

Practice

3 609,304,049

(a) Write the number in words.

(b) The value of the digit in the one millions place is _____.

(c) The value of the digit in the one thousands place is _____.

(d) Write the names of all the places with the digit 0.

(e) One hundred million more than 609,304,049 is _____.

(f) Ten million less than 609,304,049 is _____.

4 Write the numbers in numerals.

Two million, four hundred forty-seven thousand, sixteen	
Seventy-four million, three hundred seven	
Eighty-two million, eighty-two	
Four hundred six million, fifty-seven thousand, three	

5 (a) 60,000,000 + 2,000,000 + 50,000 + 200 + 30 + 9 = ☐

(b) 400,000,000 + 600,000 + 5,000 + 30 = ☐

(c) 203,800,062 = 200,000,000 + ☐ + 62

(d) 5,500,555 = 500 + ☐ + 55 + 500,000

6 Write the numbers in order from greatest to least.

680,125,823	680,125,283	680,521,823	608,125,823

7 Write >, <, or = in each ◯.

(a) 80,000,000 + 60,000 ◯ 50,000 + 400,000,000 + 900,000

(b) Six hundred twenty millions ◯ 60 hundred thousands

(c) Eight hundred millions ◯ 800,000 thousands

(d) 60,832,000 − 10,000 ◯ 59,823,000 + 10,000,000

Challenge

8 (a) 4 millions = ☐ hundred thousands

(b) 4 millions = ☐ ten thousands

(c) 4 millions = ☐ thousands

(d) 4 millions = ☐ hundreds

(e) 4 ten millions = ☐ ten thousands

(f) 4 hundred millions = ☐ hundred thousands

(g) 4 hundred millions = ☐ thousands

9 Write the numbers in numerals.

430 thousand thousands	
9,860 ten thousands	
60 thousand thousands, 40 hundred hundreds	
8 ten thousands, 56 hundred thousands, 8 ones	
8,000 ones + 12,000 tens + 4 millions	
4,000 tens + 3,000 thousands + 6,000 ones + 50,000 ten thousands	

Basics

1

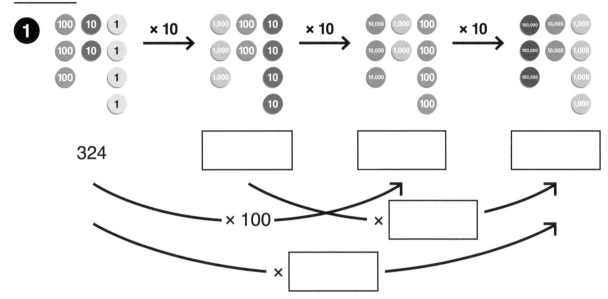

324

2 (a) 324 × 1 = [ ]

(b) 324 × 10 = [ ]

(c) 3,240 × 10 = [ ]

(d) 32,400 × 10 = [ ]

(e) 324 × 100 = [ ]

(f) 3,240 × 100 = [ ]

(g) 324 × 1,000 = [ ]

3 (a) 6,201 × 10 × 10 × 10 = 6,201 × 1,000 = [ ]

(b) 80,620 × 10 × 10 = 80,620 × 100 = [ ]

Practice

 (a) 245 × 100 = [ ]

(b) 1,080 × 10 = [ ]

(c) 100 × 6,230 = [ ]

(d) 3,240 × 100 = [ ]

(e) 400,000 × 10 = [ ]

(f) 700 × 1,000 = [ ]

(g) 420 × 1,000 = [ ]

(h) 1,000 × 6,004 = [ ]

5 (a) 85 × [ ] = 85,000

(b) 430 × [ ] = 43,000

(c) [ ] × 40 = 40,000

(d) [ ] × 7,200 = 72,000

(e) 1,000 × [ ] = 100,000

(f) [ ] × 100 = 60,000

Challenge

6 There are 1,000 paper clips in a box. The boxes are packed in crates with 100 boxes of paper clips in each crate. How many paper clips are in 100 crates?

7 (a) 10 × 10 × 10 × 10 × 10 = [ ]

(b) 100 × 10 × 100 = [ ]

(c) 40 × 10 × 100 = [ ]

(d) 100 × 10,000 × 80 = [ ]

Basics

1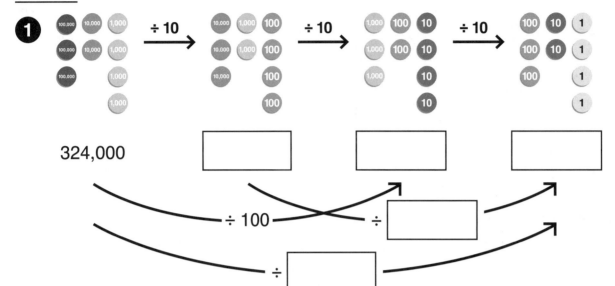

324,000

$\div\ 100$

$\div$ ☐

$\div$ ☐

2 (a) $3{,}240 \div 10 =$ ☐

(b) $32{,}400 \div 10 =$ ☐

(c) $324{,}000 \div 10 =$ ☐

(d) $32{,}400 \div 100 =$ ☐

(e) $324{,}000 \div 100 =$ ☐

(f) $324{,}000 \div 1{,}000 =$ ☐

3 (a) $56{,}000 \div 100 = \dfrac{}{100} =$ ☐

(b) $5{,}600{,}000 \div 1{,}000 = \dfrac{}{1{,}000} =$ ☐

Practice

4 (a) $1,300 \div 10 = $ ☐

(b) $8,200 \div 100 = $ ☐

(c) $98,000 \div 100 = $ ☐

(d) $62,000 \div 10 = $ ☐

(e) $400,000 \div 10 = $ ☐

(f) $720,000 \div 100 = $ ☐

(g) $920,000 \div 1,000 = $ ☐

(h) $3,090,000 \div 100 = $ ☐

5 (a) $8,500,000 \div$ ☐ $= 85,000$

(b) $620,000 \div$ ☐ $= 62,000$

(c) ☐ $\div 1,000 = 4,500$

6 A supplier paid $71,000 for 1,000 portable photo printers. How much did the supplier pay for each portable photo printer?

Challenge

7 For a Box Tops for Education program, purchasing 1,000 participating products with Box Tops logos and scanning the receipts is worth $100. If 630 students each uploaded 100 Box Top scans, how much money will the school receive?

8 (a) $100,000,000 \div 10 \div 10 \div 10 \div 10 = \boxed{}$

(b) $20,000,000 \div 10 \div 100 = \boxed{}$

(c) $3,400,000 \div 1,000 \div 100 = \boxed{}$

(d) $700,000,000 \div 10,000 \div 100 = \boxed{}$

Basics

1 (a) 31 × 5 ones = [ ] ones = [ ]

(b) 31 × 5 tens = [ ] tens = [ ]

(c) 31 × 5 hundreds = [ ] hundreds = [ ]

(d) 31 × 5 thousands = [ ] thousands = [ ]

2 (a) 28 × 4 = [ ]

(b) 28 × 40 = 28 × 4 × 10

= [ ] × 10

= [ ]

(c) 28 × 400 = 28 × 4 × 100

= [ ] × 100

= [ ]

(d) 28 × 4,000 = 28 × 4 × 1,000

= [ ] × 1,000

= [ ]

3 (a) $5 \times 8 =$ ☐

(b) $5{,}000 \times 8 = 8 \times 5{,}000$

$=$ ☐

(c) $5{,}000 \times 8{,}000 = 5{,}000 \times 8 \times 1{,}000$

$=$ ☐ $\times 1{,}000$

$=$ ☐

Practice

4 (a) $35 \times 20 =$ ☐

(b) $350 \times 2 =$ ☐

(c) $35 \times 200 =$ ☐

(d) $350 \times 20 =$ ☐

(e) $35 \times 2{,}000 =$ ☐

(f) $3{,}500 \times 20 =$ ☐

(g) $3{,}500 \times 200 =$ ☐

(h) $3{,}500 \times 2{,}000 =$ ☐

5 (a) $7 \times 400 =$

(b) $5 \times 8{,}000 =$

(c) $41 \times 6{,}000 =$

(d) $25 \times 40{,}000 =$

(e) $800 \times 9{,}000 =$

(f) $7{,}000 \times 800 =$

(g) $32{,}000 \times 400 =$

(h) $2{,}100 \times 500 =$

(i) $25{,}000 \times 600 =$

(j) $10{,}600 \times 900 =$

6 New Zealand has a population of about 4 million people. There are about 20 times as many sheep in New Zealand as people. About how many sheep are in New Zealand?

Basics

1 (a) $850 \div 5 = 85$ tens $\div 5$

$=$ [   ] tens

$=$ [   ]

(b) $8,500 \div 5 = 85$ hundreds $\div 5$

$=$ [   ] hundreds

$=$ [   ]

(c) $85,000 \div 5 = 85$ thousands $\div 5$

$=$ [   ] thousands

$=$ [   ]

2 (a) $40,000 \div 8,000 = 40,000 \div 1,000 \div 8$

$=$ [   ] $\div 8$

$=$ [   ]

(b) $40,000 \div 800 = 40,000 \div 100 \div 8$

$=$ [   ] $\div 8$

$=$ [   ]

(c) $40{,}000 \div 80 = 40{,}000 \div 10 \div 8$

$$= \boxed{} \div 8$$

$$= \boxed{}$$

3 (a) $56{,}000 \div 700 = \dfrac{56{,}000}{700} = \dfrac{\boxed{}}{7} = \boxed{}$

(b) $5{,}600{,}000 \div 7{,}000 = \dfrac{\boxed{}}{7{,}000} = \dfrac{\boxed{}}{7} = \boxed{}$

(c) $80{,}000 \div 500 = \dfrac{\boxed{}}{500} = \dfrac{\boxed{}}{5} = \boxed{}$

(d) $960{,}000 \div 80 = \dfrac{\boxed{}}{80} = \dfrac{\boxed{}}{8} = \boxed{}$

Practice

4 (a) $96 \div 6 = \boxed{}$

(b) $9{,}600 \div 600 = \boxed{}$

(c) $960{,}000 \div 600 = \boxed{}$

(d) $960{,}000 \div 6{,}000 = \boxed{}$

(e) $9{,}600{,}000 \div 6{,}000 = \boxed{}$

5 (a) $630{,}000 \div 9{,}000 = $ ☐

(b) $32{,}000 \div 400 = $ ☐

(c) $4{,}800{,}000 \div 6{,}000 = $ ☐

(d) $810{,}000{,}000 \div 9{,}000 = $ ☐

(e) $360{,}000{,}000 \div 600 = $ ☐

(f) $300{,}000 \div 600 = $ ☐

(g) $100{,}000 \div 4{,}000 = $ ☐

(h) $120{,}000 \div 5{,}000 = $ ☐

6 A grocer paid $4,500 for 300 bushels of apples. How much did 1 bushel of apples cost?

Check

1 (a) The digit 7 is in the _____ place in the number 378,903,400.

(b) The digit _____ is in the ten thousands place in the number 24,302,627.

(c) The value of the digit 2 in 542,390,108 is _____.

(d) 3,000,000 has _____ thousands.

(e) 53,900,000 has _____ ten thousands.

(f) The value of the digit 6 in 460 ten thousands is _____.

(g) 100 more than one million is the number _____.

(h) 1 less than one million is the number _____.

(i) 1 billion is _____ times more than 1 million.

(j) 6,500,000 is 100 times as great as _____.

2 Write >, <, or = in each $\bigcirc$.

(a) 5,983,426 $\bigcirc$ 5,983,416

(b) Seventy million, six hundred forty-seven thousand $\bigcirc$ 240,674,000

(c) 80,000 + 40,000,000 + 900 $\bigcirc$ 40,800,000 + 9,000

3 (a) $904{,}190 \times 100 = \boxed{}$

(b) $9{,}000 \times 400 = \boxed{}$

(c) $1{,}600 \times 5{,}000 = \boxed{}$

(d) $1{,}200{,}000 \div 100 = \boxed{}$

(e) $154{,}000 \div 700 = \boxed{}$

(f) $6{,}020{,}000 \div 20{,}000 = \boxed{}$

4 Using each digit from 0 to 8 only once, write the least 9-digit odd number with 7 in the ten thousands place.

Challenge

5 Write >, <, or = in each ◯.

(a) $50 \times 80 \times 100 \times 10$ ◯ $10 \times 100 \times 1{,}000 \times 4$

(b) $960{,}000 \times 8$ ◯ $960{,}000{,}000 \div 800$

6 (a) In 57,598,851, if the digit 7 is replaced by the digit 5, the new number is _____ less than the old number.

(b) In 460,381,974, the value of the digit in the hundred millions place is _____ times the value of the digit in the ten thousands place.

Chapter 2 Writing and Evaluating Expressions

Basics

> In general, calculate from left to right.
> Find the value in parentheses first.

1 75 craft sticks are required to make a large box, and 25 craft sticks are required to make a small box. Aisha is making sets that include one large and one small box. How many sets could she make with 500 craft sticks?

Total craft sticks ÷ Number of craft sticks per set

= 500 ÷ ([   ] + [   ])

= 500 ÷ [   ]

= [   ]

2 (a) 800 − 120 + 250

     = [   ] + 250

     = [   ]

(b) 800 − (120 + 250)

     = 800 − [   ]

     = [   ]

(c) 320 ÷ 4 × 5

     = [   ] × 5

     = [   ]

(d) 320 ÷ (4 × 5)

     = 320 ÷ [   ]

     = [   ]

Practice

3 Find the values.

(a) 400 − 53 − 27

(b) 400 − (53 − 27)

(c) 81 ÷ 9 ÷ 3

(d) 81 ÷ (9 ÷ 3)

(e) 180 ÷ (2 × 3)

(f) 4 × (60 − 22)

(g) 10,000 ÷ (48 ÷ 6)

(h) 640,000 ÷ (7,000 − 3,000)

4 Jamal had a package of 200 pipe cleaners. He made 3 woven baskets. Each basket used 35 pipe cleaners. Write an expression to find the number of pipe cleaners he has left, and then find the value.

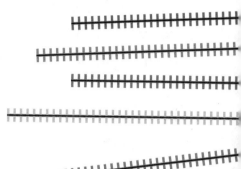

Challenge

5 In each of the following, use each of the numbers 9, 3, and 3 once to make the equations true.

(a) ☐ × ☐ ÷ ☐ = 9

(b) ☐ ÷ ☐ − ☐ = 0

(c) ☐ × (☐ − ☐) = 0

(d) ☐ × (☐ ÷ ☐) = 9

(e) ☐ − ☐ − ☐ = 3

(f) ☐ ÷ (☐ × ☐) = 1

(g) ☐ + (☐ − ☐) = 9

(h) ☐ − ☐ + ☐ = 9

Basics

> In general, calculate from left to right.
> Do multiplication and/or division first.
> Then do addition and/or subtraction.

1 Jett is making 2 boxes and 3 picture frames using craft sticks. Each box requires 125 sticks and each picture frame requires 75 sticks. How many craft sticks does he need?

Number of sticks for box + Number of sticks for frame

$=$ 2 × 125 + 3 × 75

$=$ ☐ + ☐

$=$ ☐

2 (a) 15 + 500 ÷ 2

= 15 + ☐

= ☐

(b) 4 × 2 − 10 ÷ 5

= ☐ − ☐

= ☐

(c) 54 − 8 × 5 + 10

= 54 − ☐ + 10

= ☐ + 10

= ☐

(d) 75 − 420 ÷ 7 + 3 × 15

= 75 − ☐ + ☐

= ☐ + ☐

= ☐

Practice

3 Find the values.

(a) $64 - 3 \times 9$

(b) $200 - 125 \div 25$

(c) $200 + 25 \times 4$

(d) $75 \div 5 - 4 \times 3$

(e) $30 + 24 \div 4 - 2$

(f) $88 + 18 \div 3 - 4 \times 6$

(g) $10 + 12 \times 8 - 108 \div 9 + 6$

(h) $5{,}000 - 360{,}000 \div 400 + 12{,}000$

4 At a banquet, there are 45 tables that can seat 6 people and 82 tables that can seat 8 people. Write an expression to find the total number of seats, and then find the value.

Challenge

5 Write +, −, or × between each number to make each equation true.

(a) 5   5   5   5   5 = 100

(b) 1   2   3   4   5   6   7   8   9 = 100

Basics

> In general, calculate from left to right.
>
> If there are parentheses, find the value in parentheses first.
>
> Do multiplication and/or division first, then addition and/or subtraction.

1 (a) $105 - 15 \div 3 \times 6 + 4 \div 2$

$= 105 - \boxed{} \times 6 + 4 \div 2$

$= 105 - \boxed{} + 4 \div 2$

$= 105 - 30 + \boxed{}$

$= \boxed{} + 2$

$= \boxed{}$

(b) $(105 - 15 \div 3) \times (6 + 4) \div 2$

$= (105 - \boxed{}) \times (6 + 4) \div 2$

$= \boxed{} \times (6 + 4) \div 2$

$= 100 \times \boxed{} \div 2$

$= \boxed{} \div 2$

$= \boxed{}$

(c) $(105 - 15) \div 3 \times (6 + 4 \div 2)$

$= \boxed{} \div 3 \times (6 + 4 \div 2)$

$= 90 \div 3 \times (6 + \boxed{})$

$= 90 \div 3 \times \boxed{}$

$= \boxed{} \times 8$

$= \boxed{}$

(d) $105 - (15 \div 3) \times (6 + 4) \div 2$

$= 105 - \boxed{} \times (6 + 4) \div 2$

$= 105 - 5 \times \boxed{} \div 2$

$= 105 - \boxed{} \div 2$

$= 105 - \boxed{}$

$= \boxed{}$

Practice

2 Find the values.

(a) $80 \div 8 \times 2 - 6 \div 2$

(b) $80 \div (8 \times 2 - 6) \div 2$

(c) $25 + 25 \div 5 \times 5 \div 25 - 5$

(d) $4 \times 4 \times (4 + 4 \div 4) \div 4 - 4 \times 4 + 4$

(e) $9{,}000 \div (1{,}800 \div 30 \times 20 \div 4)$

3 Andrei has 1,000 craft sticks. He used 250 craft sticks to make a boat. Then he made some birdhouses that each required 35 sticks for the base and 15 sticks for the roof. He used all of his craft sticks. Write an expression to find the number of birdhouses he made, and then find the value.

Challenge

4 Write +, −, ×, or ÷ in the $\bigcirc$ to make each equation true.

(a) $12 - 8 \div 4 \bigcirc 3 = 6$

(b) $12 \div (8 \bigcirc 4) + 4 = 5$

(c) $(12 - 8 \bigcirc 4) \times 4 = 0$

(d) $12 \bigcirc (8 \bigcirc 4 \times 2) = 3$

5 Write +, −, ×, ÷, or ( ) between the numbers to make each equation true.

(a) 4   4   4   4 = 0

(b) 4   4   4   4 = 1

(c) 4   4   4   4 = 2

(d) 4   4   4   4 = 3

(e) 4   4   4   4 = 4

(f) 4   4   4   4 = 5

(g) 4   4   4   4 = 6

(h) 4   4   4   4 = 7

(i) 4   4   4   4 = 8

(j) 4   4   4   4 = 9

Basics

1 Charlotte made 11 large picture frames and 11 small picture frames using craft sticks. The large picture frames each required 75 sticks and the small frames each required 35 sticks. We can find the total number of craft sticks she used in two different ways:

$11 \times (75 + 35)$ 　　or　　 $11 \times 75 + 11 \times 35$

$= 11 \times \boxed{}$ 　　　　　　$= 825 + \boxed{}$

$= \boxed{}$ 　　　　　　　　$= \boxed{}$

Write the missing numbers.

$11 \times (75 + 35) = \boxed{} \times 75 + 11 \times \boxed{}$

2 $3{,}998 \times 45 = (4{,}000 - 2) \times 45$

$= \boxed{} \times 45 - \boxed{} \times 45$

$= \boxed{} - \boxed{}$

$= \boxed{}$

3 $25 \times 59 = 25 \times (60 - 1)$

$= 25 \times \boxed{} - 25 \times \boxed{}$

$= \boxed{} - \boxed{}$

$= \boxed{}$

4 $125 \times 8 = (100 + \boxed{}) \times 8$

$= \boxed{} \times 8 + \boxed{} \times 8$

$= \boxed{} + \boxed{}$

$= \boxed{}$

Practice

5 Find the values. Think of ways to simplify the calculation first.

(a) 7×199

(b) $4 \times 9{,}125$

(c) 25×38

(d) $42 \times 32 + 42 \times 68$

6 Write >, <, or = in the ◯ to make each equation true.

(a) 78×54 ◯ $78 \times 50 + 78 \times 4$

(b) $8 \times 38 - 8 \times 9$ ◯ 8×28

(c) 63×5 ◯ $(60 \times 5) - (3 \times 5)$

(d) $(700 - 3) \times 7$ ◯ 7×697

(e) $3{,}009 \times 9$ ◯ $3{,}000 \times 9 \times 9 + 9$

(f) $27 \times 8 + 6 \times 8$ ◯ $(27 + 8) \times 6$

Challenge

7 (a) $7{,}925 \times 8 = (8{,}000 - 100 + \boxed{}) \times 8$

$= \boxed{} \times 8 - \boxed{} \times 8 + \boxed{} \times 8$

$= \boxed{} - \boxed{} + \boxed{}$

$= \boxed{}$

(b) $4{,}799 \times 6 = (5{,}000 - \boxed{} - 1) \times 6$

$= \boxed{} \times 6 - \boxed{} \times 6 - \boxed{} \times 6$

$= \boxed{} - \boxed{} - \boxed{}$

$= \boxed{}$

Exercise 5

Basics

1 Dana, Jett, and Charlotte used 2,085 craft sticks for their art projects. Charlotte used 215 less than 3 times as many craft sticks as Jett. Jett used 75 more craft sticks than Dana. How many craft sticks did Dana use?

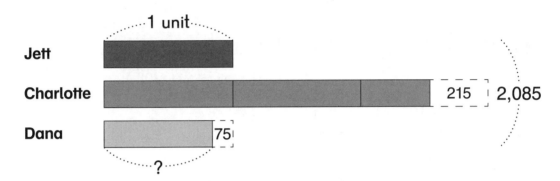

5 units $\longrightarrow$ 2,085 + ☐ + ☐ = ☐

1 unit $\longrightarrow$ ☐ ÷ 5 = ☐

Number of craft sticks Dana used:

☐ − 75 = ☐

Dana used _____ craft sticks.

2 Holly and Carlos together have $137. Ella and Carlos together have $261. Ella has 3 times as much money as Holly. How much money does Carlos have?

$137

| Carlos | Holly |

$261

| Carlos | | Ella | |

? ⟶ 1 unit

2 units ⟶ 261 − 137 = ☐

1 unit ⟶ ☐ ÷ 2 = ☐

Amount Carlos has: 137 − ☐ = ☐

Carlos has $_____.

3 An armchair cost $122 more than a couch. Andrei bought 2 armchairs and 1 couch for $1,078. How much did the couch cost?

Couch

Armchair

Armchair $1,078

$122

3 units ⟶ 1,078 − (2 × ☐) = ☐

1 unit ⟶ ☐ ÷ 3 = ☐

The couch cost $_____.

Practice

4 The total weight of 3 full suitcases is 127 lb. The gray suitcase weighs 11 lb more than the pink suitcase. The pink suitcase weighs 5 lb less than the blue suitcase. How much does the blue suitcase weigh?

5 A carry-on bag costs $24 less than a suitcase. Janice bought 3 suitcases and 2 carry-on bags for $547. How much does one suitcase cost?

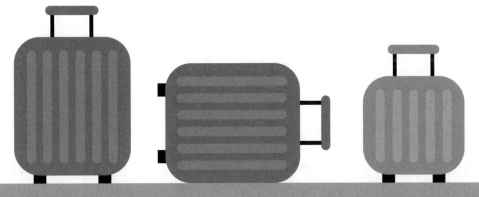

6 Three teams scored 4,050 points during a competition. Team A scored 326 points less than Team B. Team C scored twice as much as Team A and Team B combined. How many points did Team B score?

7 Callista bought a bag of 80 polished stones for $19. She also bought necklace chains for $35. She made as many necklaces as she could using the stones. Each necklace had 3 stones. She sold the necklaces for $9 each. How much did she earn from selling the necklaces after accounting for what she spent on the material?

Challenge

8 Mia, Xavier, and Micah have a total of $248. Mia and Xavier together have $165. Xavier and Micah together have $128. How much money do each of them have?

9 In a pet store, five goldfish cost as much as two tropical fish. If 10 goldfish cost $20, how many tropical fish could someone buy for $40?

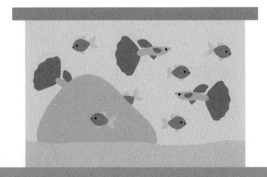

Basics

1 Maria collected 630 more ornaments than her cousin. After she gave 90 ornaments to her cousin, she had 3 times as many ornaments as her cousin. How many ornaments did Maria have at first?

Since we know that Maria had 3 times as many ornaments as her cousin after she gave ornaments to her cousin, we can draw that model first.

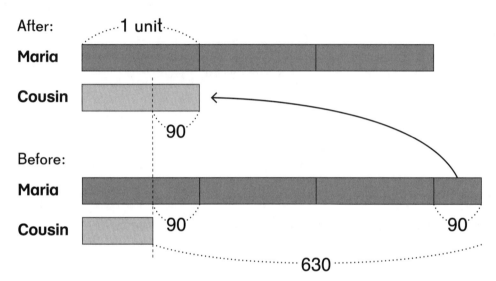

2 units ⟶ 630 − 2 × 90 = ☐

1 unit ⟶ ☐ ÷ 2 = ☐

3 units ⟶ 3 × ☐ = ☐

Number of ornaments Maria had before:

☐ + 90 = ☐

Maria had _____ ornaments at first.

2 Nolan and Susma have 156 game cards altogether. Nolan had twice as many game cards as Susma. He gave some of his game cards to Susma so that they now each have the same number of game cards. How many game cards does Susma have now?

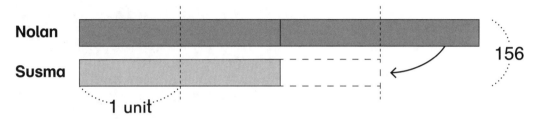

6 units $\longrightarrow$ 156

3 units $\longrightarrow$ ☐ ÷ 2 = ☐

Susma now has _____ game cards.

3 Samuel had 4 times as many coins as Arman. They both received 34 more coins. They now have a total of 458 coins. How many coins does Arman have now?

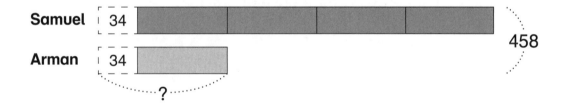

Practice

4 2 dresses and 4 shirts cost $64. 2 dresses and 7 shirts cost $85. How much do 3 dresses and 3 shirts cost?

5 Sharif and his sister had the same amount of money. After Sharif spent $75 and his sister spent $37, his sister had 3 times as much money as Sharif. How much money did Sharif have at first?

6 Nora and Renata had an equal number of polished stones at first. After Nora received 65 more stones and Renata lost 23 stones, Nora had three times as many stones as Renata. How many stones did they have altogether at first?

7 Tank A had 4 times as much water as Tank B. After 30 L of water was transferred from Tank A to Tank B, Tank B had 24 more L of water than Tank A. How much water is in both tanks altogether?

Challenge

8 4 children collected a total of 529 seashells. Then, Logan found 26 more seashells. Mila doubled her seashells. Noah lost 42 seashells. Olivia lost half of her seashells. All 4 children now have an equal number of seashells. How many seashells did Noah have to begin with?

9 3 friends divided some strawberries equally. After they each ate 4 strawberries, the total number of strawberries left was equal to the amount each friend had at the beginning. How many strawberries were there at first?

Check

1 Find the values.

(a) $72 \div (5 + 4) \times 6$

(b) $42 \div 7 \times 3 - 11 + 9$

(c) $76 + 24 \div 12 \times 7 - 26$

(d) $11 + 56 \div 8 \times 24$

(e) $36 \div (28 - 2 \times 8) \div 3$

(f) $44 - 24 \div 4 + 3 \times 5$

(g) $101 + 8 \times (12 - 4) - 3 + 15$

2 (a) $42 \times 87 = 42 \times 90 - 42 \times \boxed{}$

(b) $113 \times 456 + 113 \times 544 = 113 \times \boxed{}$

(c) $312 \times 3{,}002 = 312 \times \boxed{} + \boxed{} \times 2$

3 Use each of the given numbers once to make each equation true.

(a) 1, 2, 3, 4

$$\left(\boxed{} + \boxed{} \right) + \left(\boxed{} - \boxed{} \right) = 4$$

(b) 2, 3, 4, 5

$$\left(\boxed{} - \boxed{} \right) + \left(\boxed{} \times \boxed{} \right) = 7$$

(c) 1, 2, 4, 5, 7

$$\boxed{} \times \left(\boxed{} + \boxed{} \right) = \boxed{} + \boxed{}$$

4 2 ropes are the same length. After cutting 50 m from Rope A and 14 m from Rope B, Rope B is 3 times as long as Rope A. Find the length of Rope B.

5 Diego spent $3,100 on a laptop, a VR headset, and a gaming mouse. The laptop cost $1,900 more than the mouse and VR headset combined. The VR headset cost 3 times as much as the mouse. How much did the VR headset cost?

6 Patrick had 2,000 ducks and chickens on his farm. He had 3 times as many chickens as ducks. After selling some chickens, he now has twice as many ducks as chickens. How many chickens did he sell?

Challenge

7 4 stools cost as much as 3 chairs. 5 stools cost $28 more than 2 chairs. How much do 2 stools and 2 chairs cost?

8 Write +, −, ×, ÷, or ( ) between the numbers to make each equation true.

(a) 5   5   5   5   5 = 1

(b) 5   5   5   5   5 = 2

(c) 5   5   5   5   5 = 3

(d) 5   5   5   5   5 = 4

(e) 5   5   5   5   5 = 5

(f) 5   5   5   5   5 = 6

(g) 5   5   5   5   5 = 7

(h) 5   5   5   5   5 = 8

(i) 5   5   5   5   5 = 9

(j) 5   5   5   5   5 = 10

Chapter 3 Multiplication and Division

Basics

1 (a) Estimate the product of 627 and 38.

627 × 38
↓   ↓

[   ] × [   ] = [   ]

(b) Find the product of 627 and 38.

```
        6  2  7
  ×        3  8
  ┌──┬──┬──┬──┬──┐
  │  │  │ 0│  │ 6│  ← 627 × 8
  ├──┼──┼──┼──┼──┤
  │  │8,│  │  │ 0│  ← 627 × 30
  ├──┼──┼──┼──┼──┤
  │  │  │  │  │  │
  └──┴──┴──┴──┴──┘
```

2 (a) Sofia estimated the product of 819 and 26 to be 24,000. With what numbers could she have replaced each factor?

(b) Emma estimated the product of 819 and 26 to be 20,000. With what numbers could she have replaced each factor?

(c) Whose estimate will be closer to the actual product?

(d) Find the product of 819 and 26.

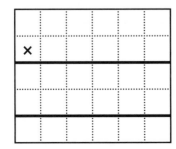

Practice

3 One of these numbers is equal to 844 × 95. Use estimation to determine which one, and circle it.

| 8,110 | 72,210 | 80,180 | 101,820 |

4 Which of the following gives the greatest product? Circle it.

| 87 × 594 | 6 × 5,594 | 12 × 1,698 |

5 Estimate, and then find the exact product.

(a) 79 × 67 ≈ ⬚

79 × 67 = ⬚

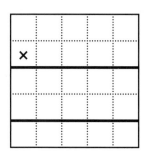

(b) 982 × 72 ≈ ⬚

982 × 72 = ⬚

(c) 638 × 48 ≈ [ ]

638 × 48 = [ ]

(d) 88 × 608 ≈ [ ]

88 × 608 = [ ]

6 The manager of an apartment complex bought new washing machines and dryers for each of the 52 apartments. The washing machines cost $398 each and the dryers cost $367 each. What was the total cost for all of the appliances he bought?

7 (a) What is the ones digit of the product of 8 and 9?

(b) What is the ones digit of the product of 948 and 79?

Challenge

8 To find the answer to 897 × 24, Melissa multiplied 900 by 24 and then subtracted. What number did she subtract?

9 Is the product of 26 × 19 × 87 odd or even? What is the ones digit of the product? Find the answer without doing the complete calculation.

Basics

1 (a) Estimate the product of 8,427 and 58.

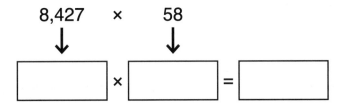

(b) Find the product of 8,427 and 58.

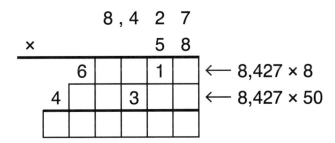

Practice

2 One of these numbers is equal to 1,899 × 89. Use estimation to determine which one, and circle it.

| 126,411 | 169,011 | 1,691,011 | 16,480 |

3 Which of the following give a product greater than 100,000? Circle them.

| 6,427 × 14 | 7,873 × 39 | 15 × 18,972 |

4 Estimate and then find the exact product.

(a) 7,814 × 24 ≈ ⬚

     7,814 × 24 = ⬚

(b) 9,026 × 81 ≈ ⬚

     9,026 × 81 = ⬚

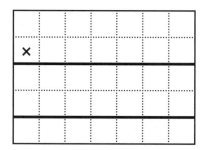

(c) 9,879 × 54 ≈ ⬚

     9,879 × 54 = ⬚

(d) 14,038 × 37 ≈ ⬚

     14,038 × 37 = ⬚

5 The manager of an apartment complex bought new refrigerators, ovens, and dishwashers for each of the 52 apartments. The refrigerators cost $598 each, the ovens cost $388 each, and the dishwashers cost $298 each. What is the total cost of all of these appliances?

Challenge

6 Multiply.

(a) 879 × 406

(b) 4,027 × 36,040

Exercise 3

Check

1 Multiply and use the answers to complete the cross number puzzle on the next page.

Across

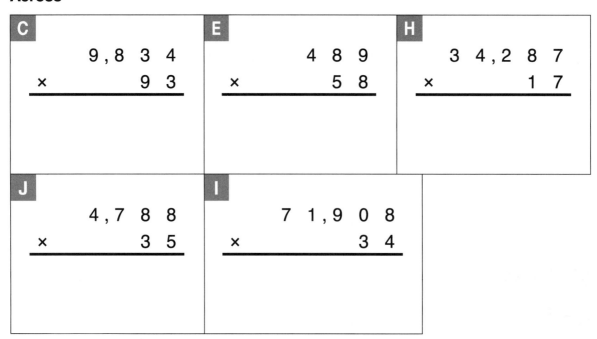

C
```
    9 , 8  3  4
 ×         9  3
 ─────────────
```

E
```
        4  8  9
 ×         5  8
 ─────────────
```

H
```
    3 4 , 2  8  7
 ×            1  7
 ─────────────
```

J
```
    4 , 7  8  8
 ×         3  5
 ─────────────
```

I
```
    7 1 , 9  0  8
 ×            3  4
 ─────────────
```

Down

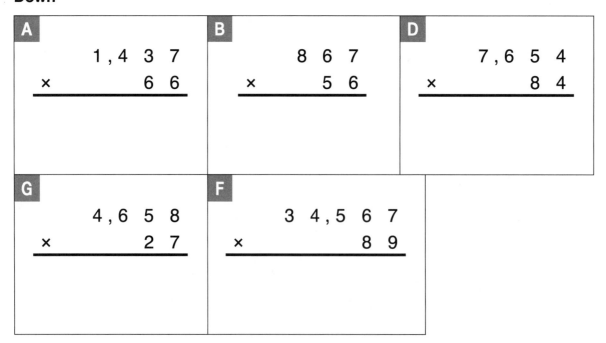

A
```
    1 , 4  3  7
 ×         6  6
 ─────────────
```

B
```
        8  6  7
 ×         5  6
 ─────────────
```

D
```
    7 , 6  5  4
 ×         8  4
 ─────────────
```

G
```
    4 , 6  5  8
 ×         2  7
 ─────────────
```

F
```
    3 4 , 5  6  7
 ×            8  9
 ─────────────
```

2 Write > or < in each ◯. Use estimation.

(a) 8,268 × 42 ◯ 320,000

(b) 1,689 × 84 ◯ 200 × 900

(c) 2,724 × 12 ◯ 270 × 100

(d) 394 × 56 ◯ 15,873 + 8,699

(e) 1,198 × 18 ◯ 781 × 49

(f) 8,107 × 11 ◯ 148,107 − 62,876

3 Alicia paid $1,690 per month for rent in the first year. The second year, her rent increased by $55 a month. How much did she pay in rent for those two years?

4 The manager of an apartment complex bought water heaters for each of the 52 apartments. The water heaters each cost $1,398. It cost $832 to install each water heater. The electrician installing the water heaters gave a $3,400 discount on the total. What was the cost of buying and installing the water heaters?

Challenge

5 Look for a pattern in the following problems. Find the product for the first problem. Can you can think of an easy way to find the next product by using the product of the previous expression? Explain. Then find the products for the rest for the problems.

$5{,}812 \times 37 =$ ☐

$5{,}815 \times 37 =$ ☐

$5{,}818 \times 37 =$ ☐

$5{,}821 \times 37 =$ ☐

$5{,}824 \times 37 =$ ☐

6 Find the missing digits.

(a)

```
          4, ☐ ☐ ☐
  ×          9 ☐
  ─────────────────
      3 ☐ ☐ ☐ ☐ 1
    4 0 ☐ 1 7 0
  ─────────────────
    4 3 ☐ ☐ ☐ ☐ 1
```

(b)

```
            7, ☐ ☐ 5
  ×              ☐ ☐
  ─────────────────────
       2 ☐ 1 ☐ ☐
     ☐ 8 ☐   ☐ 0 ☐
  ─────────────────────
   3 0 3, ☐ 9 5
```

Basics

1 Make groups of 4 tens.

There are _____ groups of 4 tens with _____ ten left over.

130 ÷ 40 is [   ] R [   ]

2 (a) Complete the following estimations for the quotient of 400 ÷ 70.

350 ÷ 70 = [   ]   420 ÷ 70 = [   ]

(b) Divide 400 by 70.

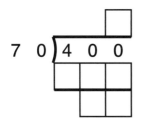

3 (a) Complete the following estimations for the quotient of 896 ÷ 90.

810 ÷ 90 = [   ]   900 ÷ 90 = [   ]

(b) Divide 896 by 90.

$$9\,0\,\overline{)8\;9\;6}$$

Practice

 Divide.

(a) 762 ÷ 80

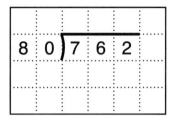

(b) 438 ÷ 70

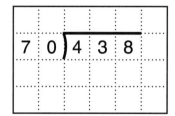

(c) 385 ÷ 50

(d) 651 ÷ 90

(e) 700 ÷ 80

(f) 600 ÷ 70

5 200 pieces of paper are distributed equally among 30 students. How many pieces of paper will each student get, and how many are left over?

6 Use mental calculation to find the quotients and remainders.

   (a) 430 ÷ 70   (b) 180 ÷ 50

   (c) 290 ÷ 30   (d) 420 ÷ 80

Challenge

7 What will be the ones digit of the remainder for each of these divisions?

   (a) 789 ÷ 20   (b) 972 ÷ 70

8 Divide.

   (a) 3,256 ÷ 20   (b) 40,287 ÷ 60

Basics

1 Divide 87 by 21.

Emma estimated: $80 \div 20 = 4$

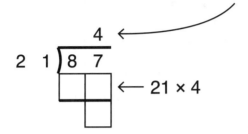

2 Divide 86 by 24.

Dion estimated: $80 \div 20 = 4$

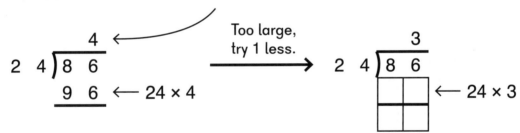

3 Divide 71 by 16.

Alex estimated: $60 \div 20 = 3$

Practice

4 Divide.

(a) 98 ÷ 31

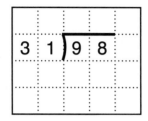

(b) 71 ÷ 52

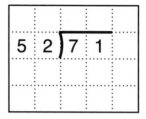

(c) 91 ÷ 13

(d) 61 ÷ 22

(e) 76 ÷ 23

(f) 58 ÷ 14

5 52 cards are dealt out to 12 players. How many cards does each player get? How many cards are left over?

Basics

1 Divide 371 by 49.

Mei estimated: 350 ÷ 50 = 7

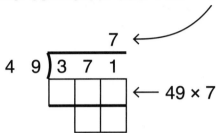

← 49 × 7

2 Divide 345 by 38.

Sofia estimated: 320 ÷ 40 = 8

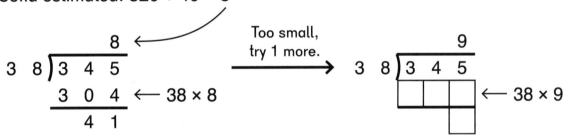

3 Divide 165 by 24.

Emma estimated: 160 ÷ 20 = 8

```
        8     Too large,        7     Too large,        6
2 4 )1 6 5     try 7.     2 4 )1 6 5     try 6.    2 4 )1 6 5
    1 9 2        ———>        1 6 8        ———>
```

Practice

4 Divide.

(a) 653 ÷ 86

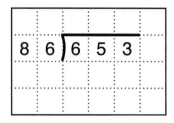

(b) 511 ÷ 73

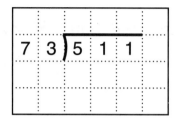

(c) 389 ÷ 47

(d) 815 ÷ 82

(e) 320 ÷ 53

(f) 406 ÷ 68

5 A farmer collected 195 eggs. He put some of them into 2 cartons of 12, and put the rest into cartons of 18. How many full cartons of 18 did he have?

Basics

1 Divide 893 by 28.

89 is greater than 28, so the quotient will start in the _____ place.

Divide 89 tens by 28.
90 tens ÷ 30 = 3 tens. Try 3 tens.

```
        3
  2 8 )8 9 3
       8 4      ← 28 × 3 tens
     ───────
         5
```

Divide 53 by 28.
60 ÷ 30 = 2. Since 28 × 2 = 56, 2 is too large. Try 1.

```
        3 □
  2 8 )8 9 3
       8 4
     ───────
         5 3
        □ □
      ───────
        □ □
```

Check your answer:

2 Divide 852 by 21.

```
        4 □
  2 1 )8 5 2
       □ □
      ───────
        □ □
```

Check your answer:

Practice

3 In each of the following problems, put a check mark in the place where the quotient will start.

(a)

$$24\overline{)590}$$

(b)

$$43\overline{)902}$$

(c)

$$63\overline{)570}$$

(d)

$$56\overline{)553}$$

4 Divide.

(a) $971 \div 29$

(b) $702 \div 29$

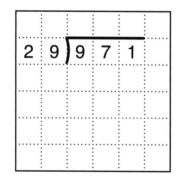

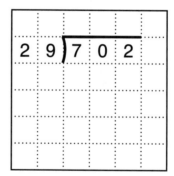

(c) $772 \div 37$

(d) $945 \div 15$

5 The area of a rectangle is 444 in². One side measures 1 foot. What is the length of the other side in inches?

Challenge

6 To divide 851 by 16, Alex first estimated that the tens digit of the quotient was 4. When he found it was too small (since the remainder was 21) he replaced the tens digit of the quotient with a 5. Instead of then erasing the 64 and multiplying 16 by 5 and then finding the new remainder, he subtracted 16 from the 21 and then proceeded. Does this work, and if so, why?

```
              5
             4  3
    1 6 ) 8  5  1
           6  4
           2  1
           1  6
              5  1
              4  8
                 3
```

Basics

1 (a) Divide 787 by 32.

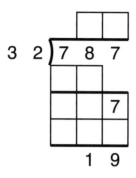

(b) Divide 7,876 by 32.

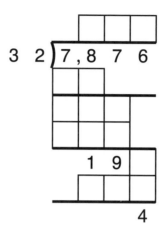

(c) Check your answer for 7,876 ÷ 32:

2 (a) Divide 941 by 23.

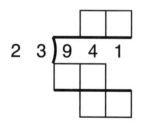

(b) Divide 9,413 by 23.

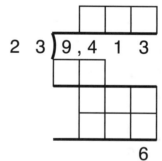

(c) Check your answer for 9,413 ÷ 23:

3 (a) Divide 487 by 52.

$$5\,2\,\overline{)\,4\quad8\quad7}$$

(b) Divide 4,872 by 52.

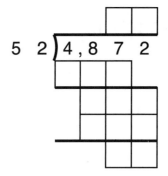

$$5\,2\,\overline{)\,4\,,8\quad7\quad2}$$

(c) Check your answer for 4,872 ÷ 52:

Practice

4 In each of the following problems, put a check mark in the place where the quotient will start.

(a)

$$4\,5\,\overline{)\,8\,,8\quad2\quad7}$$

(b)

$$6\,3\,\overline{)\,5\,,9\quad0\quad7}$$

(c)

$$3\,4\,\overline{)\,6\,,8\quad0\quad9}$$

(d)

$$4\,6\,\overline{)\,4\,,2\quad3\quad2}$$

5 Divide.

(a) 7,716 ÷ 19

(b) 8,072 ÷ 28

(c) 5,728 ÷ 63

(d) 9,285 ÷ 15

(e) 7,056 ÷ 85

(f) 8,297 ÷ 60

Check

1 Divide.

(a) $889 \div 30$

(b) $460 \div 53$

(c) $982 \div 28$

(d) $1{,}010 \div 11$

(e) $8{,}932 \div 29$

(f) $6{,}285 \div 18$

2 Write > or < in each ◯. Use estimation.

(a) $937 \div 8$ ◯ $3{,}270 \div 40$

(b) $5{,}938 \div 62$ ◯ $4{,}812 \div 36$

(c) $8{,}908 \div 17$ ◯ 132×7

(d) $8{,}107 \div 11$ ◯ $128{,}107 - 72{,}876$

3 Express 152 ounces as pounds and ounces.

4 Lee's pickup truck can carry up to 1,500 lb. Lee weighs 195 lb and there are 45 lb of other contents in the truck. How many 94-pound bags of cement can the truck carry?

5 A rope 10 m long is cut into 4 parts. Part B is 4 times as long as Part A, and Part C is 4 times as long as part B. Part D is 55 cm long. How long is Part C?

6 The manager of a new apartment complex with 12 apartments spent $8,190 on bathroom and kitchen sinks for each unit. Half of the units had 2 bathrooms. Each kitchen sink cost twice as much as each bathroom sink. What was the cost of 1 bathroom sink?

Challenge

7 When a 3 digit number is divided by 11, the remainder is greater than the quotient. What is the number?

8 When 165 is divided by a 2-digit divisor, the remainder is 30. What is the divisor?

9 Find the missing digits.

(a)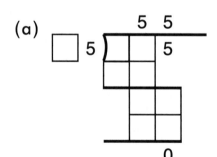

(b)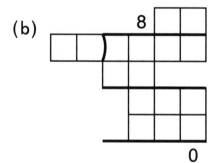

Chapter 4 Addition and Subtraction of Fractions

Basics

1 (a) Divide 2 by 5.

$2 \div 5 = \boxed{}$

(b) Divide 37 by 5.

$$\begin{array}{r} 7 \\ 5\overline{)3\ 7} \\ \underline{3\ 5} \\ 2 \end{array}$$

37 ÷ 5 is 7 with a remainder of 2.

Divide the remainder by 5: $2 \div 5 = \boxed{}$

$37 \div 5 = 7 + \boxed{} = \boxed{}\boxed{}$

(c) Divide 762 by 5. Express the answer as a mixed number.

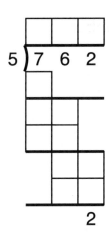

$762 \div 5 = \boxed{}\boxed{}$

2 Express $\frac{15}{2}$ as a mixed number in simplest form.

$$\frac{15}{2} = \boxed{}\,\boxed{\frac{}{}}$$

3 Express $\frac{63}{4}$ as a mixed number in simplest form.

$$\frac{63}{4} = 63 \div 4 = \boxed{}\,\boxed{\frac{}{}}$$

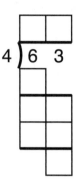

4 Express $\frac{146}{12}$ as a mixed number in simplest form.

(a) $\frac{146}{12} = 146 \div 12 = \boxed{}\,\boxed{\frac{}{12}} = \boxed{}\,\boxed{\frac{}{}}$

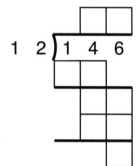

(b) Simplify $\frac{146}{12}$ and then express it as a mixed number.

$$\frac{146}{12} = \boxed{\frac{}{6}} = \boxed{} \div 6 = \boxed{}\,\boxed{\frac{}{}}$$

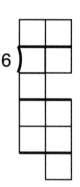

5 $140 \div 21 = \boxed{} \div 3 = \boxed{}\,\boxed{\frac{}{}}$

Practice

6 Express each fraction as a mixed number in simplest form.

(a) $\dfrac{99}{5}$

(b) $\dfrac{250}{6}$

(c) $\dfrac{119}{14}$

(d) $\dfrac{740}{15}$

7 Divide. Express each answer as a mixed number in simplest form.

(a) $35 \div 4$

(b) $930 \div 8$

(c) $260 \div 25$

(d) $4,900 \div 90$

8 How many pounds is 100 ounces?

Basics

1 Add $\frac{1}{3}$ and $\frac{2}{5}$.

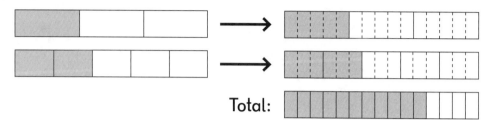

$$\frac{1}{3} + \frac{2}{5} = \frac{5}{15} + \boxed{\frac{}{}} = \boxed{\frac{}{}}$$

2 Add $\frac{3}{8}$ and $\frac{1}{6}$.

(a) $8 \times 6 = 48$. 48 is a common multiple of 8 and 6.

$$\frac{3}{8} + \frac{1}{6} = \frac{3 \times 6}{8 \times 6} + \frac{1 \times 8}{6 \times 8} = \boxed{\frac{}{48}} + \boxed{\frac{}{48}} = \boxed{\frac{}{48}} = \boxed{\frac{}{24}}$$

(b) The least common multiple of 8 and 6 is 24.

$$\frac{3}{8} + \frac{1}{6} = \frac{3 \times 3}{8 \times 3} + \frac{1 \times 4}{6 \times 4} = \boxed{\frac{}{24}} + \boxed{\frac{}{24}} = \boxed{\frac{}{24}}$$

3 Add $\frac{3}{7}$ and $\frac{2}{3}$.

$$\frac{3}{7} + \frac{2}{3} = \boxed{\frac{}{21}} + \boxed{\frac{}{21}} = \boxed{\frac{}{21}} = \boxed{\frac{}{}}$$

Practice

 Add. Express each answer in simplest form.

(a) $\frac{3}{4} + \frac{3}{20}$

(b) $\frac{1}{6} + \frac{3}{10}$

(c) $\frac{1}{6} + \frac{4}{15}$

(d) $\frac{5}{12} + \frac{3}{4}$

(e) $\frac{6}{7} + \frac{1}{2}$

(f) $\frac{5}{6} + \frac{8}{9}$

(g) $\frac{1}{2} + \frac{2}{5} + \frac{1}{3}$

(h) $\frac{3}{4} + \frac{5}{6} + \frac{2}{3}$

5 Jaiden practiced the violin for $\frac{2}{3}$ h on Monday, $\frac{5}{6}$ h on Tuesday, and $\frac{3}{4}$ h each on Wednesday and Thursday. How long did he practice the violin altogether?

Challenge

6 Complete each problem using the given digits. Fractions should all be less than 1 and in simplest form.

(a) 1, 2, 5, 9

$$\boxed{\frac{}{}} + \boxed{\frac{2}{}} = \boxed{\frac{}{10}}$$

(b) 1, 2, 2, 5, 10

$$\boxed{\frac{}{}} + \boxed{\frac{}{}} = \boxed{\frac{9}{}}$$

(c) 1, 7, 8, 12, 24

$$\boxed{\frac{}{}} + \boxed{\frac{}{}} = \boxed{\frac{5}{}}$$

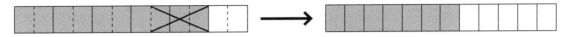

Exercise 3

Basics

1 Subtract $\frac{1}{4}$ from $\frac{5}{6}$.

$$\frac{5}{6} - \frac{1}{4} = \frac{10}{12} - \boxed{} = \boxed{}$$

2 Subtract $\frac{7}{10}$ from $\frac{5}{6}$.

(a) $6 \times 10 = 60$. 60 is a common multiple of 6 and 10.

$$\frac{5}{6} - \frac{7}{10} = \frac{5 \times 10}{6 \times 10} - \frac{7 \times 6}{10 \times 6} = \boxed{\frac{}{60}} - \boxed{\frac{}{60}} = \boxed{\frac{}{60}} = \boxed{}$$

(b) The least common multiple of 6 and 10 is 30.

$$\frac{5}{6} - \frac{7}{10} = \frac{5 \times 5}{6 \times 5} - \frac{7 \times 3}{10 \times 3} = \boxed{\frac{}{30}} - \boxed{\frac{}{30}} = \boxed{\frac{}{30}} = \boxed{}$$

3 Subtract $\frac{5}{16}$ from 1.

$$1 - \frac{5}{16} = \boxed{\frac{}{}} - \frac{5}{16} = \boxed{\frac{}{16}}$$

Practice

 Subtract. Express each answer in simplest form.

(a) $\frac{3}{5} - \frac{3}{15}$

(b) $\frac{3}{4} - \frac{5}{12}$

(c) $\frac{1}{2} - \frac{3}{7}$

(d) $\frac{7}{12} - \frac{3}{8}$

(e) $\frac{1}{6} - \frac{1}{10}$

(f) $1 - \frac{6}{21}$

(g) $1 - \frac{2}{5} - \frac{1}{3}$

(h) $\frac{7}{8} - \frac{1}{6} - \frac{2}{3}$

5 Louis bought $\frac{3}{4}$ kg of flour. He used $\frac{3}{10}$ kg to bake bread. How many kilograms of flour does he have left?

Challenge

6 Study the following examples.

$$\frac{1}{2} - \frac{1}{3} = \frac{1 \times 3}{2 \times 3} - \frac{1 \times 2}{3 \times 2} = \frac{3 - 2}{2 \times 3} = \frac{1}{6}$$

$$\frac{1}{3} - \frac{1}{4} = \frac{1 \times 4}{3 \times 4} - \frac{1 \times 3}{4 \times 3} = \frac{4 - 3}{3 \times 4} = \frac{1}{12}$$

$$\frac{1}{4} - \frac{1}{5} = \frac{1 \times 5}{4 \times 5} - \frac{1 \times 4}{5 \times 4} = \frac{5 - 4}{4 \times 5} = \frac{1}{20}$$

Use a quick method to find the following values.

(a) $\frac{1}{9} - \frac{1}{10}$

(b) $\frac{1}{99} - \frac{1}{100}$

(c) $\frac{1}{19} - \frac{1}{20}$

Check

1 Express each fraction as a mixed number in simplest form.

(a) $\dfrac{26}{6}$

(b) $\dfrac{50}{8}$

(c) $\dfrac{455}{25}$

(d) $\dfrac{1,220}{100}$

2 Divide. Express each answer as a mixed number in simplest form.

(a) $98 \div 3$

(b) $100 \div 80$

(c) $500 \div 6$

(d) $155 \div 15$

3 Find the values. Express each answer in simplest form.

(a) $\frac{2}{3} + \frac{1}{8}$

(b) $\frac{7}{15} + \frac{5}{6}$

(c) $\frac{9}{10} - \frac{2}{3}$

(d) $\frac{11}{12} - \frac{5}{9}$

(e) $\frac{9}{10} - \left(\frac{1}{3} + \frac{1}{2}\right)$

(f) $\frac{9}{10} - \frac{1}{3} + \frac{1}{2}$

(g) $\frac{2}{5} - \left(\frac{2}{5} - \frac{1}{3}\right)$

(h) $\frac{9}{14} + \frac{2}{3} - \frac{1}{7}$

4 $\frac{1}{5}$ of a pole is painted green, $\frac{1}{3}$ of it is painted yellow, and $\frac{1}{6}$ of it is painted blue. The rest of it is painted red. What fraction of the pole is painted red?

5 Elena had 12 kg of flour. She used $\frac{1}{2}$ kg for bread, $\frac{1}{3}$ kg for rolls, and $\frac{1}{6}$ kg for cake. She then divided the rest of the flour into 5 containers. How much flour is in each container?

Challenge

6 Find the value.

$$\frac{1}{2} - \frac{1}{3} + \frac{1}{3} - \frac{1}{4} + \frac{1}{4} - \frac{1}{5} + \frac{1}{5} - \frac{1}{6} + \frac{1}{6} - \frac{1}{7}$$

Basics

1. Fill in the blanks for each problem. Each problem uses a different strategy to add the given numbers.

(a) $8\frac{2}{3} + \frac{3}{4} = 8\frac{\boxed{}}{12} + \frac{\boxed{}}{12}$

$= 8\frac{\boxed{}}{12}$

$= 9\frac{\boxed{}}{\boxed{}}$

(b) $5\frac{1}{2} + \frac{5}{8} = 5\frac{4}{8} + \frac{\boxed{}}{\boxed{}}$

$= 5\frac{4}{8} + \frac{4}{8} + \frac{\boxed{}}{\boxed{}}$

$= 6\frac{\boxed{}}{8}$

(c) $1\frac{1}{3} + \frac{3}{5} = \frac{\boxed{}}{3} + \frac{3}{5}$

$= \frac{\boxed{}}{15} + \frac{\boxed{}}{15}$

$= \frac{\boxed{}}{15}$

$= \boxed{}\frac{\boxed{}}{\boxed{}}$

Practice

 Add. Use any method. Express each answer in simplest form.

(a) $4\frac{4}{9} + \frac{5}{9}$

(b) $6\frac{5}{12} + \frac{11}{12}$

(c) $3\frac{7}{8} + \frac{3}{4}$

(d) $\frac{2}{5} + 8\frac{1}{4}$

(e) $\frac{5}{9} + 4\frac{1}{2}$

(f) $9\frac{5}{8} + \frac{2}{3}$

(g) $\frac{3}{4} + \frac{1}{2} + 1\frac{5}{8}$

(h) $\frac{1}{3} + 3\frac{1}{6} + \frac{3}{4}$

Basics

1 Fill in the blanks for each problem.

(a) $3\frac{7}{12} + 4\frac{2}{3} = 7\frac{7}{12} + \frac{2}{3}$

$$= 7\frac{7}{12} + \boxed{\frac{}{12}}$$

$$= 7\boxed{\frac{}{12}}$$

$$= \boxed{}\boxed{\frac{}{12}}$$

$$= \boxed{}\boxed{\frac{}{}}$$

(b) $1\frac{1}{2} + 2\frac{4}{5} = \boxed{\frac{}{2}} + \boxed{\frac{}{5}}$

$$= \boxed{\frac{}{10}} + \boxed{\frac{}{10}}$$

$$= \boxed{\frac{}{10}}$$

$$= \boxed{}\boxed{\frac{}{}}$$

Practice

 Add. Use any method. Express each answer in simplest form.

(a) $4\frac{3}{8} + 2\frac{5}{8}$

(b) $4\frac{5}{7} + 4\frac{3}{7}$

(c) $1\frac{1}{6} + 9\frac{7}{12}$

(d) $3\frac{9}{11} + 2\frac{1}{2}$

(e) $3\frac{9}{10} + 3\frac{5}{6}$

(f) $12\frac{5}{6} + 7\frac{3}{8}$

(g) $2\frac{1}{3} + \frac{3}{5} + 3\frac{2}{5}$

(h) $2\frac{1}{2} + 3\frac{1}{3} + 4\frac{1}{4} + 5\frac{1}{5} + 6\frac{1}{6}$

3 Last week, Calli bought $3\frac{3}{4}$ m of cloth. This week, she bought $1\frac{1}{5}$ m more cloth than what she bought last week. How many meters of cloth did she buy altogether?

Challenge

4 Use each of the digits 0 to 9 once to form two mixed numbers with a sum of 100.

This is one possible solution:

$$29\frac{1}{3} + 70\frac{56}{84}$$

Find another solution.

Basics

1 Fill in the blanks for each problem. Each problem uses a different strategy to subtract the given numbers.

(a) $7\frac{1}{3} - \frac{3}{4} = 7\dfrac{\boxed{}}{12} - \dfrac{\boxed{}}{12}$

$\phantom{7\frac{1}{3} - \frac{3}{4}} = 6\dfrac{\boxed{}}{12} - \dfrac{\boxed{}}{12}$

$\phantom{7\frac{1}{3} - \frac{3}{4}} = 6\dfrac{\boxed{}}{\boxed{}}$

(b) $3\frac{2}{9} - \frac{2}{3} = 3 - \frac{2}{3} + \frac{2}{9}$

$\phantom{3\frac{2}{9} - \frac{2}{3}} = 2\dfrac{\boxed{}}{3} + \frac{2}{9}$

$\phantom{3\frac{2}{9} - \frac{2}{3}} = 2\dfrac{\boxed{}}{9} + \frac{2}{9}$

$\phantom{3\frac{2}{9} - \frac{2}{3}} = \boxed{}\dfrac{\boxed{}}{\boxed{}}$

(c) $2\frac{1}{4} - \frac{5}{7} = \dfrac{\boxed{}}{4} - \frac{5}{7}$

$\phantom{2\frac{1}{4} - \frac{5}{7}} = \dfrac{\boxed{}}{28} - \dfrac{\boxed{}}{28}$

$\phantom{2\frac{1}{4} - \frac{5}{7}} = \dfrac{\boxed{}}{28}$

$\phantom{2\frac{1}{4} - \frac{5}{7}} = \boxed{}\dfrac{\boxed{}}{\boxed{}}$

Practice

2 Subtract. Use any method. Express each answer in simplest form.

(a) $7\frac{4}{7} - \frac{5}{7}$

(b) $6\frac{5}{6} - \frac{5}{12}$

(c) $8\frac{5}{12} - \frac{1}{4}$

(d) $4\frac{1}{3} - \frac{5}{6}$

(e) $5\frac{7}{10} - \frac{5}{6}$

(f) $9\frac{2}{15} - \frac{5}{6}$

(g) $12 - \frac{3}{5} - \frac{1}{2}$

(h) $8\frac{1}{3} - \frac{5}{6} - \frac{2}{9}$

Basics

1 Fill in the blanks for each problem.

(a) $7\frac{7}{12} - 3\frac{3}{4} = 4\frac{7}{12} - \frac{3}{4}$

$= 4\frac{7}{12} - \dfrac{\boxed{}}{12}$

$= 3\dfrac{\boxed{}}{12} - \dfrac{\boxed{}}{12}$

$= 3\dfrac{\boxed{}}{12}$

$= \boxed{}\dfrac{\boxed{}}{}$

(b) $2\frac{3}{4} - 1\frac{1}{12} = \dfrac{\boxed{}}{4} - \dfrac{\boxed{}}{12}$

$= \dfrac{\boxed{}}{12} - \dfrac{\boxed{}}{12}$

$= \dfrac{\boxed{}}{12}$

$= \dfrac{\boxed{}}{}$

$= \boxed{}\dfrac{\boxed{}}{}$

Practice

2 Subtract. Use any method. Express each answer in simplest form.

(a) $4\frac{3}{8} - 2\frac{5}{8}$

(b) $7\frac{9}{14} - 2\frac{3}{7}$

(c) $9\frac{3}{8} - 6\frac{7}{12}$

(d) $2\frac{2}{9} - 1\frac{2}{3}$

(e) $6\frac{5}{6} - 3\frac{3}{10}$

(f) $12\frac{3}{9} - 7\frac{5}{6}$

(g) $12\frac{1}{3} - 3 - 2\frac{3}{5}$

(h) $7\frac{1}{4} - 2\frac{1}{5} - 2\frac{3}{10}$

Exercise 9

Check

1 Find the values. Express each answer in simplest form.

(a) $4\frac{3}{8} - \frac{3}{4}$

(b) $7\frac{4}{5} + \frac{4}{15}$

(c) $9\frac{3}{8} + 2\frac{5}{12}$

(d) $3\frac{3}{7} - 1\frac{1}{2}$

(e) $9\frac{1}{3} - (3\frac{5}{6} - 2\frac{1}{2})$

(f) $9\frac{1}{3} - 3\frac{5}{6} - 2\frac{1}{2}$

2 (a) _____ $+ 2\frac{1}{3} = 5\frac{1}{4}$

(b) _____ $- 3\frac{1}{2} = 5\frac{1}{6}$

3 A container has $4\frac{3}{5}$ L of water. $1\frac{7}{10}$ L is needed to fill it to full capacity. What is the capacity of the container in liters?

4 Wainani's time for running 100 m was $18\frac{1}{3}$ seconds. Taylor's time was $3\frac{4}{5}$ s less than Wainani's time. What was Taylor's time for running 100 m?

5 To make blended coffee, a barista mixed 12 lb of beans from Ecuador with 15 lb of beans from Kenya. He then divided the blend into 8 equal portions and added $1\frac{3}{4}$ lb of beans from Colombia to each bag. What is the weight of coffee in each bag?

6 A rectangle is $3\frac{1}{4}$ ft long and $2\frac{1}{3}$ ft wide. What is the perimeter in feet?

7 A spider climbed $7\frac{1}{4}$ inches up a wall, then slid down $1\frac{1}{2}$ inches, and then climbed another $5\frac{3}{8}$ inches. How much higher did the spider end up from its starting place?

Challenge

8 Find the value.

$$10\frac{1}{7} - 9\frac{1}{8} + 9\frac{1}{8} - 8\frac{1}{9} + 8\frac{1}{9} - 7\frac{1}{10} + 7\frac{1}{10} - 6\frac{1}{11} + 6\frac{1}{11} - 10\frac{1}{12}$$

Check

1 (a) Put commas in the correct places, then write the number in words.

4 0 7 1 4 8 0 0 0

(b) The value of the digit in the hundred millions place is _____ times the value of the digit in the ten thousands place.

(c) If the digit 7 is replaced by the digit 5, the new number is _____ less than the old number.

2 What is the greatest odd number that is less than 7,000,000 + 30,000 + 20?

3 A condo is sold at $589,000 when rounded to the nearest $1,000. What is the greatest possible price for the condo, in whole dollars?

4 (a) ☐ ÷ 600 = 400

(b) 900 × ☐ = 108,000

(c) 28,800 ÷ ☐ = 400

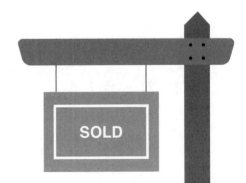

5 Find the values. Express fractions in simplest form.

(a) $6 \times (3 + 2) - 8$

(b) $15 - 8 \times 3 \div 2 + 6$

(c) $2{,}000 \div (100 + 300 \div 15 \times 20)$

(d) $72 \times 63 + 28 \times 63$

(e) $4{,}999 \times 19$

(f) $(70 + 12) \div 12$

(g) $8{,}560 \div 32$

(h) $72 \div (7 - \frac{1}{2} - \frac{1}{3} - \frac{1}{6})$

(i) $6\frac{1}{4} - 3\frac{5}{6} + 2\frac{1}{3}$

(j) $6\frac{1}{4} - (3\frac{5}{6} + 1\frac{1}{3})$

6 Patrick bought 12 chairs and 3 tables for $819. Each table cost 3 times as much as each chair. How much did 1 table cost?

7 A shopkeeper ordered 75 cans of a special brand of tea. Each can holds 50 packets of tea. Each packet costs $2, and the can costs $4. The shipping cost is $25. How much did the shopkeeper pay?

8 A blue cable is 7 m long. It is $1\frac{4}{5}$ m longer than a yellow cable. The yellow cable is $3\frac{3}{4}$ m longer than a black cable. How long is the black cable in meters?

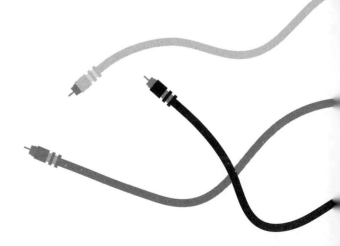

9 At first, Rita and Kim had $200 altogether. After Rita spent $62 and Kim spent $46, Kim had 3 times as much money as Rita. How much money did Kim have at first?

10 Daniela is 11 years old. Her brother is 3 years older than she is. In how many years will their combined age be 55 years?

Challenge

11 Write the greatest possible whole number that will make the following true.

$$16 \times (\boxed{} - 11) < 1{,}999$$

12 Use mental calculation to find the values.

(a) $499{,}991 + 29{,}996 + 7{,}997 + 598 + 69$

(b) $3{,}689 - (2{,}489 + 899)$

13 Santino has 9 bills that total $100. The bills are all 5-dollar bills, 10-dollar bills, or 20-dollar bills. How many of each kind of bill does he have?

14 The below expression is a way to express 26 with 5 twos, using whole numbers, fractions, and the symbols +, −, ×, ÷, and ( ).

$$26 = 2 \times \left(\frac{22}{2} + 2\right)$$

All the numbers from 1 to 26 can be expressed with 5 twos, except 17. Express as many numbers from 1 to 25 with 5 twos as you can. Express 17 with 6 twos.

$$1 = 2 + 2 - 2 - \frac{2}{2}$$

Chapter 5 Multiplication of Fractions

Basics

1 Find the value of 4 groups of $\frac{7}{10}$.

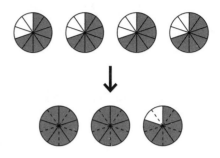

$$4 \times \frac{7}{10} = \frac{\overset{2}{\cancel{4}} \times 7}{\underset{5}{\cancel{10}}}$$

$$= \boxed{\frac{}{5}}$$

$$= \boxed{}\,\boxed{\frac{}{}}$$

2 Find the product of 6 and $\frac{5}{9}$.

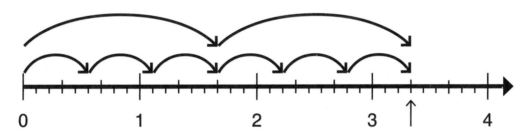

$$\overset{2}{\cancel{6}} \times \frac{5}{\underset{3}{\cancel{9}}} = \frac{2 \times 5}{3} = \boxed{\frac{}{3}} = \boxed{}\,\boxed{\frac{}{}}$$

3 $25 \times \frac{5}{8} = \boxed{\frac{}{8}} = \boxed{}\,\boxed{\frac{}{}}$

4 $16 \times \frac{5}{6} = \boxed{\frac{}{3}} = \boxed{}\,\boxed{\frac{}{}}$

Practice

5 Multiply. Express each answer in simplest form.

(a) $15 \times \frac{2}{5}$

(b) $24 \times \frac{3}{4}$

(c) $13 \times \frac{3}{7}$

(d) $10 \times \frac{3}{8}$

(e) $8 \times \frac{3}{10}$

(f) $20 \times \frac{5}{6}$

(g) $8 \times \frac{7}{20}$

(h) $15 \times \frac{5}{12}$

6 A paper clip is $\frac{7}{8}$ in long. How long are 12 paper clips placed in a row end to end?

Basics

1 Find $\frac{3}{8}$ of 24.

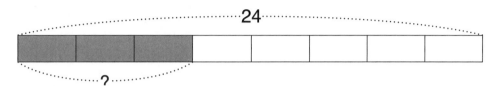

24

?

8 units ⟶ 24

1 unit ⟶ $\frac{24}{8}$

3 units ⟶ $3 \times \frac{24}{8} = \boxed{}$

2 Find $\frac{7}{10}$ of 4.

$\frac{7}{10} \times 4 = 7 \times \frac{\overset{2}{\cancel{4}}}{\underset{5}{\cancel{10}}}$

$= \dfrac{\boxed{}}{5}$

$= \boxed{}\ \boxed{\dfrac{}{}}$

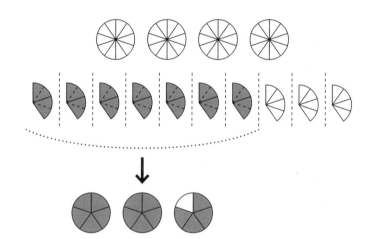

3 Find $\frac{5}{9}$ of 6.

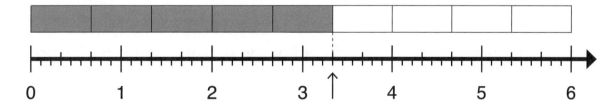

$\underset{3}{\overset{}{\frac{5}{\cancel{9}}}} \times \overset{2}{\cancel{6}} = \boxed{\dfrac{}{}} = \boxed{}\ \boxed{\dfrac{}{}}$

Practice

 Multiply. Express each answer in simplest form.

(a) $\frac{1}{9} \times 180$

(b) $\frac{3}{8} \times 56$

(c) $\frac{3}{10} \times 120$

(d) $\frac{5}{9} \times 3$

(e) $\frac{3}{4} \times 30$

(f) $\frac{7}{8} \times 20$

(g) $\frac{3}{7} \times 18$

(h) $\frac{7}{10} \times 15$

5 Stanley used $\frac{3}{4}$ of the cement in a 94-pound bag of cement. How many pounds of cement did he use?

CEMENT

94 LB

Basics

1 $\frac{2}{5}$ of the pens in a box are blue. $\frac{1}{2}$ of them are black. The rest of them are red. There are 36 more blue pens than red pens. How many pens are there altogether?

$$\frac{2}{5} = \frac{4}{10} \qquad \frac{1}{2} = \frac{5}{10}$$

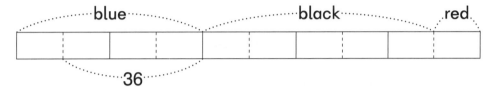

3 units ⟶ 36

1 unit ⟶ $\frac{36}{3}$ =

10 units ⟶

2 $\frac{1}{2}$ of Aurora's savings is equal to $\frac{2}{3}$ of Hazel's savings. After Hazel saved another $45, they both had the same amount of money. How much money did Aurora save?

Aurora

Hazel

$45

1 unit ⟶ 45

4 units ⟶

3 Jody had $\frac{2}{3}$ as many action figures as Aiden. After Aiden gave $\frac{1}{2}$ of his action figures to Jody, Jody had 21 action figures. How many action figures did Jody have at first?

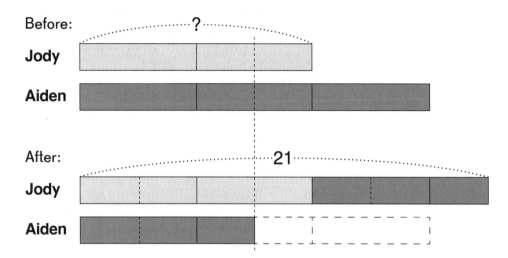

7 units ⟶ 21

1 unit ⟶ $\frac{21}{7}$ =

4 units ⟶

Practice

4 Sarah spent $\frac{2}{5}$ of her money on a keyboard. If the keyboard cost $240, how much money did she have at first?

5 There were 10 lb of flour in a bag. Alberto used $\frac{2}{5}$ of the flour for bread and $\frac{1}{4}$ of the flour for pancakes. How many pounds of flour are left?

6 Malik has $\frac{5}{8}$ as much money as Emilio. Altogether, they have $195. How much money does Emilio have?

7 Amalie had $472 in savings. She spent $105 on hiking boots and some more money on hiking poles. She has $\frac{5}{8}$ of her savings left. How much did she spend on the hiking poles?

8 A baker made 3 kinds of bagels. $\frac{3}{8}$ of them were plain bagels and $\frac{1}{5}$ of them were cheese bagels. The rest were sesame seed bagels. There were 28 fewer cheese bagels than plain bagels. How many sesame seed bagels were there?

9 $\frac{1}{4}$ of Clara's savings is equal to $\frac{2}{3}$ of Maria's savings. Clara saved $80 more than Maria. How much did Maria save?

Check

1 Find the values. Express each answer in simplest form.

(a) $35 \times \frac{3}{5}$

(b) $\frac{3}{8} \times 120$

(c) $\frac{2}{3} \times 16$

(d) $8 \times \frac{7}{12}$

(e) $36 \times \frac{3}{8}$

(f) $\frac{5}{9} \times 33$

(g) $8\frac{1}{3} + 7 \times \frac{1}{6}$

(h) $(1\frac{1}{2} - \frac{3}{4}) \times 2$

(i) $8 \times \frac{1}{3} - 6 \times \frac{1}{3}$

(j) $\frac{4}{5} \times 6 + \frac{1}{2} \times 3$

2 Jacob charged $35 a day for pet sitting. In June, he had 3 clients. He worked for the first client for $\frac{1}{5}$ of the days in the month, and for the other two clients for $\frac{3}{10}$ of the days of the month. He saved $\frac{1}{3}$ of the money he made, and spent the rest. How much money did he spend? (June has 30 days.)

3 There are 240 seats in a small drama theatre. $\frac{1}{4}$ of the seats are premium seats that cost $75. The rest are regular seats that cost $60. For one show, tickets were sold for $\frac{2}{3}$ of the premium seats and $\frac{4}{5}$ of the regular seats. How much money was received from ticket sales?

4 Three friends participated in a fund-raising project. Dexter collected $\frac{2}{5}$ of the total amount. Carter collected $272 more than Jack. Jack collected $764. How much did the three of them collect altogether?

5 There were 1,265 people at a boat show. After $\frac{1}{5}$ of the adults and $\frac{1}{3}$ of the children left, there was an equal number of children and adults at the show. How many people left the show?

Challenge

6 $297 \times \frac{26}{74}$ is closest to which of the following numbers?

| 50 | 75 | 100 | 150 | 20 |

7 Kai has some new kittens. When he was asked how many he had, he said the number of kittens he had was equal to three fourths of the total number plus three fourths of a kitten. How many kittens does he have?

8 After Josie sold $\frac{1}{4}$ of the cabbages and $\frac{3}{5}$ of the cauliflowers at the market, she had the same number of cabbages as cauliflowers left. If she sold 42 more cauliflowers than cabbages, how many cabbages did she have at first?

Basics

1 Shade the rectangle to show $\frac{1}{2}$ of $\frac{3}{5}$.

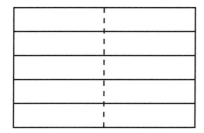

$$\frac{1}{2} \times \frac{3}{5} = \frac{1 \times 3}{2 \times 5}$$

$$= \boxed{\underline{}}$$

2 Shade the rectangle to show $\frac{1}{6}$ of $\frac{2}{3}$.

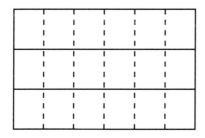

$$\frac{1}{6} \times \frac{2}{3} = \frac{1 \times 2}{6 \times 3}$$

$$= \boxed{\frac{}{18}}$$

$$= \boxed{\underline{}}$$

3 Shade the bar and draw an arrow on the number line to show $\frac{1}{6}$ of $\frac{3}{4}$.

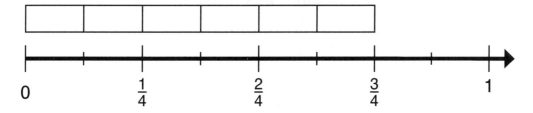

$$\frac{1}{6} \times \frac{3}{4} = \frac{1 \times 3}{6 \times 4} = \boxed{\frac{}{24}} = \boxed{\underline{}}$$

Practice

4 Find the values. Express each answer in simplest form.

(a) $\frac{1}{4} \times \frac{1}{6}$

(b) $\frac{1}{3} \times \frac{3}{5}$

(c) $\frac{1}{3} \times \frac{5}{6}$

(d) $\frac{1}{2} \times \frac{6}{7}$

(e) $\frac{1}{6} \times \frac{3}{10}$

(f) $\frac{1}{12} \times \frac{3}{4}$

(g) $\frac{1}{9} \times \frac{6}{7}$

(h) $\frac{1}{9} \times \frac{72}{100}$

5 John has a garden with an area of $\frac{4}{5}$ acres. He planted herbs in $\frac{1}{8}$ of the garden. How many acres did he plant with herbs?

Basics

1 Shade the rectangle to show $\frac{2}{3}$ of $\frac{4}{5}$.

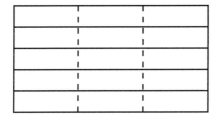

$$\frac{2}{3} \times \frac{4}{5} = \frac{2 \times 4}{3 \times 5}$$

$$= \boxed{\frac{}{}}$$

2 Shade the rectangle to show $\frac{5}{6}$ of $\frac{2}{3}$.

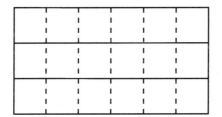

$$\frac{5}{6} \times \frac{2}{3} = \frac{5 \times 2}{6 \times 3}$$

$$= \boxed{\frac{}{18}}$$

$$= \boxed{\frac{}{}}$$

3 Shade the rectangles to show $\frac{5}{6}$ of $\frac{4}{3}$.

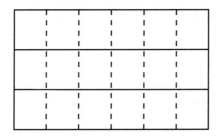

$$\frac{5}{6} \times \frac{4}{3} = \frac{5 \times 4}{6 \times 3}$$

$$= \boxed{\frac{}{18}}$$

$$= \boxed{} \boxed{\frac{}{}}$$

4 Shade the bar and draw an arrow on the number line to show $\frac{5}{6}$ of $\frac{3}{4}$.

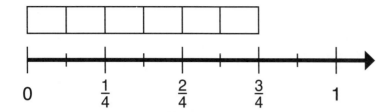

$$\frac{5}{6} \times \frac{3}{4} = \frac{5 \times 3}{6 \times 4} = \boxed{\frac{}{24}} = \boxed{\frac{}{}}$$

5 Shade the bar and draw an arrow on the number line to show $\frac{7}{6}$ of $\frac{3}{4}$.

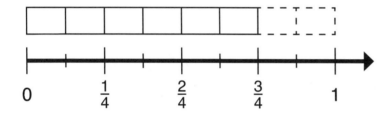

$$\frac{7}{6} \times \frac{3}{4} = \frac{7 \times 3}{6 \times 4} = \boxed{\frac{}{24}} = \boxed{\frac{}{}}$$

6 Shade the bar and draw an arrow on the number line to show $\frac{7}{6}$ of $\frac{5}{4}$.

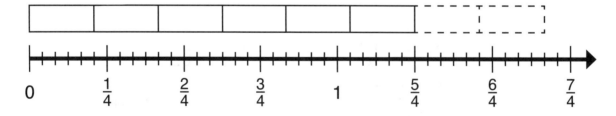

$$\frac{7}{6} \times \frac{5}{4} = \frac{7 \times 5}{6 \times 4} = \boxed{\frac{}{}} = \boxed{}\,\boxed{\frac{}{}}$$

Practice

7 Which of the following will have values greater than $\frac{2}{3}$?

$$\frac{2}{3} \times \frac{5}{6} \qquad \frac{6}{5} \times \frac{2}{3} \qquad \frac{5}{8} \times \frac{2}{3} \qquad \frac{2}{3} \times \frac{8}{5} \qquad \frac{32}{17} \times \frac{2}{3}$$

8 Find the values. Express each answer in simplest form.

(a) $\frac{3}{4} \times \frac{7}{10}$

(b) $\frac{2}{3} \times \frac{4}{7}$

(c) $\frac{2}{3} \times \frac{5}{6}$

(d) $\frac{3}{4} \times \frac{8}{11}$

(e) $\frac{7}{4} \times \frac{7}{20}$

(f) $\frac{5}{6} \times \frac{3}{2}$

(g) $\frac{3}{2} \times \frac{7}{5}$

(h) $\frac{5}{4} \times \frac{8}{5}$

Basics

1 Find $\frac{5}{6}$ of $\frac{2}{3}$.

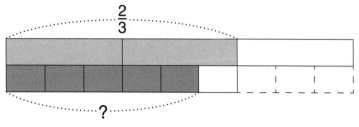

$$\frac{5}{6} \times \frac{2}{3} = \frac{5 \times \overset{1}{\cancel{2}}}{\underset{3}{\cancel{6}} \times 3} = \boxed{}$$

2 Find $\frac{8}{5}$ of $\frac{5}{12}$.

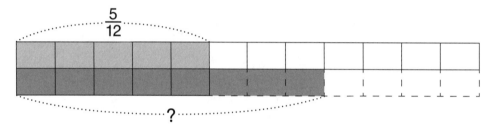

$$\frac{8}{5} \times \frac{5}{12} = \frac{\overset{2}{\cancel{8}} \times \overset{1}{\cancel{5}}}{\underset{1}{\cancel{5}} \times \underset{3}{\cancel{12}}} = \boxed{}$$

3 Find the product of $\frac{5}{9}$ and $\frac{6}{7}$.

$$\frac{5}{\underset{3}{\cancel{9}}} \times \frac{\overset{2}{\cancel{6}}}{7} = \boxed{}$$

4 Find the product of $\frac{12}{5}$ and $\frac{15}{8}$.

$$\frac{\overset{3}{\cancel{12}}}{\underset{1}{\cancel{5}}} \times \frac{\overset{3}{\cancel{15}}}{\underset{2}{\cancel{8}}} = \boxed{} = \boxed{}\boxed{}$$

Practice

5 Find the values. Express each answer in simplest form.

(a) $\frac{4}{5} \times \frac{3}{14}$

(b) $\frac{2}{3} \times \frac{4}{5}$

(c) $\frac{5}{9} \times \frac{3}{10}$

(d) $\frac{3}{8} \times \frac{4}{15}$

(e) $\frac{5}{6} \times \frac{8}{15}$

(f) $\frac{8}{3} \times \frac{9}{20}$

(g) $\frac{5}{3} \times \frac{12}{5}$

(h) $\frac{105}{104} \times \frac{16}{7}$

6 A bag of rice weighs $\frac{9}{10}$ kg. Amy used $\frac{2}{3}$ of it to make rice pudding. How many kilograms of rice did she use?

Challenge

 7 $\frac{1}{3}$ and $\frac{1}{4}$ have the same product and difference:

$$\frac{1}{3} \times \frac{1}{4} = \frac{1}{3} - \frac{1}{4}$$

Name five other pairs of numbers that have the same product and difference.

8 Fill in the blanks to make each equation true. All fractions must be less than 1 and in simplest form.

(a) $\boxed{\dfrac{3}{}} \times \boxed{\dfrac{5}{7}} = \boxed{\dfrac{3}{14}}$

(b) $\boxed{\dfrac{5}{12}} \times \boxed{\dfrac{}{15}} = \boxed{\dfrac{1}{9}}$

(c) $\boxed{\dfrac{}{21}} \times \boxed{\dfrac{}{10}} = \boxed{\dfrac{1}{6}}$

(d) $\boxed{\dfrac{8}{}} \times \boxed{\dfrac{}{10}} = \boxed{\dfrac{12}{25}}$

Basics

1 Find 4 groups of $1\frac{2}{3}$.

$4 \times 1\frac{2}{3} = 4 \times \frac{5}{3}$

$= \boxed{\rule{0pt}{1em}}$

$= \boxed{}\boxed{\rule{0pt}{1em}}$

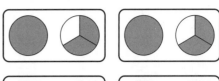
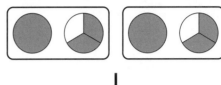

2 Shade the bar and draw an arrow on the number line to show $\frac{5}{6}$ of $1\frac{1}{4}$.

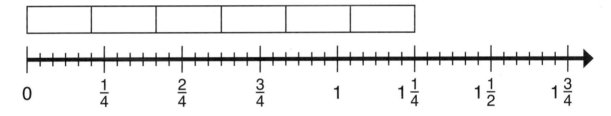

$\frac{5}{6} \times 1\frac{1}{4} = \frac{5}{6} \times \frac{5}{4} = \boxed{\rule{0pt}{1em}} = \boxed{}\boxed{\rule{0pt}{1em}}$

3 Shade the bar and draw an arrow on the number line to show $1\frac{1}{2}$ times as much as $1\frac{1}{3}$.

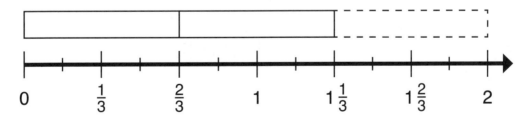

$1\frac{1}{2} \times 1\frac{1}{3} = \frac{3}{2} \times \frac{4}{3} = \boxed{}$

Practice

4 Find the values. Express each answer in simplest form.

(a) $3\frac{2}{5} \times 25$

(b) $14 \times 2\frac{4}{5}$

(c) $15 \times 2\frac{4}{9}$

(d) $\frac{4}{5} \times 3\frac{1}{8}$

(e) $1\frac{5}{6} \times \frac{5}{8}$

(f) $1\frac{1}{8} \times 3\frac{5}{9}$

(g) $2\frac{1}{7} \times 4\frac{1}{5}$

(h) $1\frac{7}{9} \times 2\frac{1}{10}$

5 Josh picked $4\frac{3}{4}$ pounds of strawberries. Mandy picked $1\frac{1}{3}$ times as many pounds of strawberries as Josh did. How many pounds of strawberries did they pick altogether?

6 25 seeds are planted. The distance between each seed is $1\frac{3}{4}$ inches. What is the distance between the first and last seed in inches?

Challenge

7 Write the digits 1, 2, or 3 in each blank space to make each equation true. All fractions must be in simplest form.

(a) $\boxed{}\boxed{\dfrac{}{}} \times \dfrac{2}{3} = \boxed{}\boxed{\dfrac{}{}}$

(b) $\boxed{}\boxed{\dfrac{}{}} \times 1\frac{2}{5} = \boxed{}\boxed{\dfrac{}{}}$

Exercise 9

Basics

1 $\frac{2}{9}$ of the buttons in a bag are green.

(a) $\frac{1}{4}$ of the green buttons have two holes and the rest have 4 holes. What fraction of the buttons are green and have 4 holes?

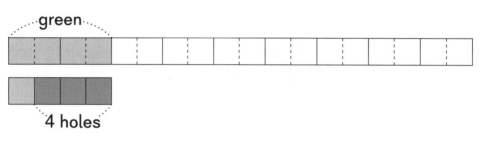

$\frac{3}{4} \times \frac{2}{9} =$

(b) $\frac{1}{2}$ of the remaining buttons are red. The rest of the buttons are brown. What fraction of the total number of buttons are brown?

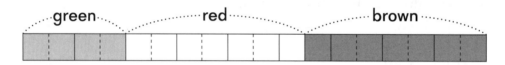

$\frac{1}{2} \times \frac{7}{9} =$

(c) There are 14 brown buttons. How many buttons are there altogether?

7 units $\longrightarrow$

1 unit $\longrightarrow$

18 units $\longrightarrow$

2 A bakery has 500 bagels. $\frac{1}{3}$ of the bagels are plain, $\frac{1}{6}$ of them are salt, $\frac{2}{5}$ of the remainder are garlic, and the rest are sesame seed. How many of the bagels are sesame seed?

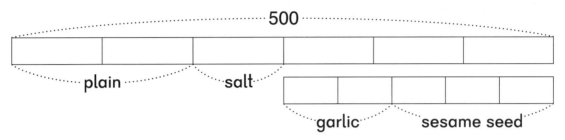

Remainder (garlic and sesame seed): $1 - (\frac{1}{3} + \frac{1}{6}) =$

Sesame seed: $\frac{3}{5} \times \frac{1}{2} \times 500 =$

3 $\frac{1}{5}$ of the passengers on a ship are men. $\frac{2}{3}$ of the remainder are women, and the rest are children. There are 234 more children than men. How many of the passengers are women?

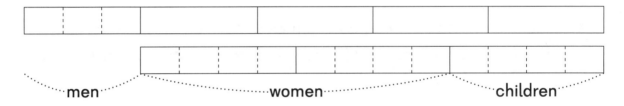

Women: $\frac{2}{3} \times \frac{4}{5} =$

Children: $\frac{1}{3} \times \frac{4}{5} =$

$\frac{4}{15} - \frac{1}{5} =$

$\frac{1}{15}$ of the total $\longrightarrow$

$\frac{8}{15}$ of the total $\longrightarrow$

Practice

4 Patrick spent $\frac{5}{6}$ of his money on camping equipment. $\frac{2}{5}$ of what he spent was for a backpack and the rest was for a tent. He had $60 left. How much did the tent cost?

5 Rosa spent $\frac{1}{4}$ of her money on a camping stove and $\frac{1}{6}$ of the remainder on a water purifier. She spent $267. How much money did she have at first?

6 Josie sold $\frac{3}{7}$ of all the ears of corn she brought to the market in the morning and $\frac{2}{3}$ of the remaining ears of corn in the afternoon. She sold 255 ears of corn in all. She donated the leftover ears of corn to the food bank. How many ears of corn did she donate to the food bank?

Challenge

7 Luisa had $5\frac{1}{2}$ kg of beans. On Monday, she used $\frac{1}{5}$ of the beans to make refried beans. On Tuesday, she used $\frac{1}{3}$ of the remaining beans to make enchiladas. On Wednesday, she used $\frac{5}{8}$ of the rest of the beans to make soup. How many kilograms of beans does she have left?

Basics

1 Find the value of 3 groups of $\frac{1}{3}$.

$3 \times \frac{1}{3} =$ ☐

$3 \times$ _____ $= 1$, so the reciprocal of 3 is _____ .

2 Shade the bar and draw an arrow on the number line to show $\frac{5}{2}$ of $\frac{2}{5}$.

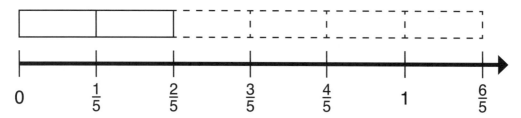

$$\frac{5}{2} \times \frac{2}{5} = \frac{\overset{1}{\cancel{5}} \times \overset{1}{\cancel{2}}}{\underset{1}{\cancel{2}} \times \underset{1}{\cancel{5}}} = \boxed{}$$

The reciprocal of $\frac{2}{5}$ is _____ .

3 Shade the bar and draw an arrow on the number line to show $\frac{4}{7}$ of $\frac{7}{4}$.

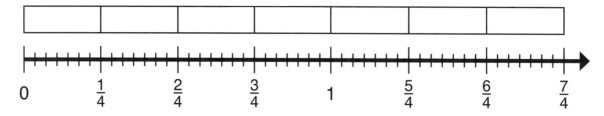

$$\frac{4}{7} \times \frac{7}{4} = \frac{\overset{1}{\cancel{4}} \times \overset{1}{\cancel{7}}}{\underset{1}{\cancel{7}} \times \underset{1}{\cancel{4}}} = \boxed{}$$

The reciprocal of $\frac{7}{4}$ is _____ .

4 Find the reciprocal of $4\frac{1}{3}$.

$$4\frac{1}{3} = \frac{\boxed{}}{3}$$

The reciprocal of $4\frac{1}{3}$ is $\boxed{\dfrac{3}{}}$.

Practice

5 Write the reciprocal of each number. Express fractions greater than 1 as imperfect fractions.

(a) $\frac{1}{8}$

(b) $\frac{7}{12}$

(c) $\frac{10}{3}$

(d) $2\frac{1}{9}$

(e) 10

(f) $2\frac{5}{8}$

6 Fill in the blanks. Express answers in simplest form.

(a) _____ $\times \frac{1}{12} = 1$

(b) $1\frac{2}{5} \times$ _____ $= 1$

(c) _____ $\times \frac{7}{10} = 1$

(d) _____ $\times 2\frac{1}{3} = 1$

(e) $\frac{1}{3} \times \frac{3}{5} \times$ _____ $= 1$

(f) $1\frac{1}{4} \times \frac{3}{5} \times$ _____ $= 1$

Check

1 Find the values. Express each answer in simplest form.

(a) $\frac{4}{9} \times \frac{1}{2}$

(b) $\frac{2}{5} \times \frac{7}{8}$

(c) $\frac{5}{6} \times \frac{6}{5}$

(d) $3 \times 3\frac{5}{9}$

(e) $1\frac{1}{6} \times 9\frac{6}{7}$

(f) $\frac{4}{5} \times \frac{3}{8} \times 20$

(g) $\frac{2}{3} + \frac{2}{5} \times \frac{1}{4}$

(h) $\frac{5}{6} \times 18 \div 4 \times \frac{1}{3}$

(i) $\frac{2}{3} \times \frac{2}{5} + \frac{1}{3} + 28 \div 6$

(j) $15 - (14 \times \frac{5}{6}) + \frac{3}{5} \times \frac{5}{6}$

2 Write the reciprocal of each value. Express fractions greater than 1 as imperfect fractions.

(a) $\frac{5}{8}$

(b) $\frac{7}{5}$

(c) $2\frac{2}{11}$

(d) $5 + 3$

(e) $\frac{1}{5} \times \frac{1}{3}$

(f) $\frac{1}{5} + \frac{1}{3}$

3 What is the sum of the reciprocals of $\frac{3}{5}$ and $\frac{2}{3}$?

4 Three identical bags of sand weigh 10 kg altogether. How many kilograms do 8 of these bags weigh?

5 How many $\frac{3}{4}$-cup scoops of flour will make 1 cup of flour?

6 On Saturday, Tomas read $\frac{1}{3}$ of his book. On Sunday, he read $\frac{2}{5}$ of what was left. What fraction of his book does he still have to read?

7 Tania had $3\frac{3}{5}$ L of juice. She drank $\frac{1}{3}$ of it on Monday, and $\frac{2}{3}$ of the remainder on Tuesday. How many liters of juice does she have left?

8 In Amy's class, $\frac{2}{3}$ of the students have pets. $\frac{3}{4}$ of the students who have pets have dogs. If 15 students have dogs, how many students are in her class?

9 A square has sides $5\frac{1}{3}$ cm long. The rectangle below is made up of $3\frac{1}{2}$ of these squares. What is the perimeter of the figure?

$5\frac{1}{3}$ cm

10 Rohan bought some tiles for a kitchen floor. $\frac{3}{5}$ of the tiles were white, $\frac{1}{4}$ of the remainder were yellow, and the rest were blue. There were 60 more white tiles than blue tiles. Each tile cost $3. What was the total cost of the tiles?

Challenge

11 A tank is $\frac{2}{3}$ full. If another 3 L of water is added, it will be $\frac{7}{8}$ full. What is the capacity of the tank?

12 A passenger fell asleep on a train halfway to his destination. He slept until he had half as far to go as the distance he traveled while he was asleep. What fraction of the trip was he sleeping?

13 A boy has as many sisters as brothers, but each sister has only half as many sisters as brothers. How many brothers and sisters are in the family?

Chapter 6 Division of Fractions

Basics

1 Divide $\frac{1}{5}$ by 2.

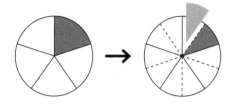

$$\frac{1}{5} \div 2 = \boxed{\frac{}{2}} \text{ of } \frac{1}{5}$$

$$= \boxed{\frac{}{2}} \times \frac{1}{5}$$

$$= \boxed{\frac{}{}}$$

2 Shade the rectangle to show $\frac{1}{2} \div 6$.

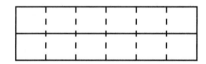

$$\frac{1}{2} \div 6 = \frac{1}{2} \times \boxed{\frac{}{}}$$

$$= \boxed{\frac{}{}}$$

3 Shade the bar and draw an arrow on the number line to show $\frac{1}{3} \div 4$.

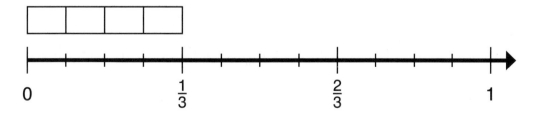

$$\frac{1}{3} \div 4 = \frac{1}{3} \times \boxed{\frac{}{}} = \boxed{\frac{}{}}$$

Practice

4 Divide.

(a) $\frac{1}{5} \div 5$

(b) $\frac{1}{8} \div 2$

(c) $\frac{1}{10} \div 10$

(d) $\frac{1}{15} \div 4$

5 (a) $\frac{1}{7} \div \boxed{} = \frac{1}{42}$

(b) $\frac{1}{3} \div \boxed{} = \frac{1}{18}$

(c) $\boxed{\dfrac{1}{}} \div 25 = \frac{1}{50}$

(d) $\boxed{\dfrac{1}{}} \div 5 = \frac{1}{100}$

6 4 sheets of plywood are $\frac{1}{2}$ in thick. How thick is 1 sheet of plywood?

7 5 racquetballs weigh $\frac{1}{4}$ kg. How many kilograms does 1 racquetball weigh?

Basics

1 Divide $\frac{2}{3}$ by 4.

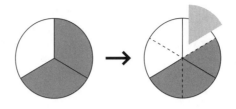

$$\frac{2}{3} \div 4 = \boxed{\frac{}{4}} \text{ of } \frac{2}{3}$$

$$= \boxed{\frac{}{4}} \times \frac{2}{3}$$

$$= \boxed{\frac{}{6}}$$

2 Shade the rectangle to show $\frac{3}{4} \div 5$.

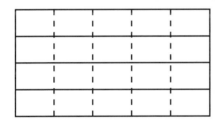

$$\frac{3}{4} \div 5 = \frac{3}{4} \times \boxed{\frac{}{}}$$

$$= \boxed{\frac{}{}}$$

3 Shade the bar and draw an arrow on the number line to show $\frac{2}{3} \div 6$.

$$\frac{2}{3} \div 6 = \frac{2}{3} \times \boxed{\frac{}{}} = \boxed{\frac{1}{}}$$

Practice

4 Divide. Express each answer in simplest form.

(a) $\frac{3}{10} \div 2$

(b) $\frac{5}{6} \div 3$

(c) $\frac{5}{8} \div 10$

(d) $\frac{6}{7} \div 9$

(e) $\frac{8}{9} \div 12$

(f) $\frac{3}{5} \div 12$

5 A regular hexagon has 6 equal sides. Its perimeter is $\frac{3}{5}$ m. How long is one side in meters?

6 Joseph bought $\frac{9}{10}$ kg of grapes. He bought 3 times as many kilograms of grapes as Paula bought. How many kilograms of grapes did Paula buy?

Challenge

7 (a) $\boxed{\dfrac{5}{}} \div 25 = \frac{1}{35}$

(b) $\boxed{\dfrac{9}{}} \div 6 = \frac{3}{20}$

Check

1 Find the values. Express each answer in simplest form.

(a) $\frac{1}{6} \div 5$

(b) $\frac{8}{9} \div 4$

(c) $\frac{3}{4} \div 6$

(d) $\frac{6}{7} \div 10$

(e) $\frac{2}{3} \div 10 \times \frac{6}{7}$

(f) $(2\frac{1}{7} \times 2\frac{1}{3}) \div 5$

(g) $(\frac{4}{5} - \frac{1}{2}) \div 3 \times 20$

(h) $(2\frac{1}{3} - \frac{5}{6} - \frac{1}{2}) \div 6 \times \frac{3}{5}$

2 Violet used $\frac{3}{4}$ of a bag of dirt to fill 6 pots. What fraction of the bag of dirt is in each pot?

3 8 identical blocks weigh $\frac{2}{5}$ kg. How many kilograms does 1 block weigh?

4 Isaiah spent $\frac{1}{3}$ of his money on a notebook and the remainder on 4 identical pencils. What fraction of his money did he spend on 1 pencil?

Challenge

5 (a) $\frac{2}{7} \div \boxed{} = \frac{1}{14}$

(b) $\frac{8}{15} \div \boxed{} = \frac{2}{45}$

6 Find the values. Express each answer in simplest form.

(a) $7\frac{1}{2} \div 2$

(b) $5\frac{3}{5} \div 8$

(c) $(5 - 1\frac{4}{7}) \div 4$

(d) $5 - 3\frac{3}{5} \div 3$

Basics

1 (a) _____ is the reciprocal of $\frac{1}{5}$.

(b) How many fifths are in 2 wholes?

$2 \div \frac{1}{5} = 2 \times \boxed{}$

$= \boxed{}$

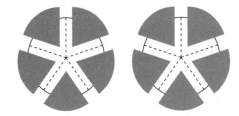

2 (a) _____ is the reciprocal of $\frac{1}{4}$.

(b) How many fourths are in 3 wholes?

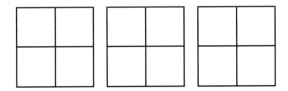

$3 \div \frac{1}{4} = 3 \times \boxed{}$

$= \boxed{}$

3 How many halves are in 6?

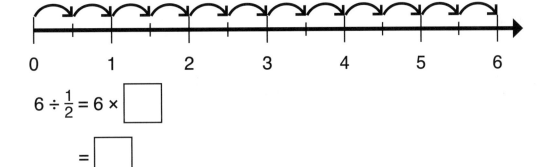

$6 \div \frac{1}{2} = 6 \times \boxed{}$

$= \boxed{}$

4. Finish labeling the tick marks on the number lines to find the answers.

(a) $\frac{1}{2}$ of what is 6?

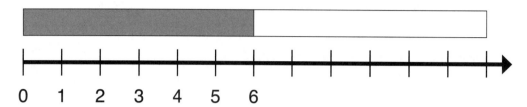

0 1 2 3 4 5 6

$\frac{1}{2} \times ? = 6$

$6 \div \frac{1}{2} = 6 \times \boxed{} = \boxed{}$

(b) 3 is $\frac{1}{3}$ of what number?

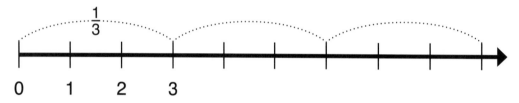

0 1 2 3

$3 \div \frac{1}{3} = 3 \times \boxed{} = \boxed{}$

Practice

5. Divide.

(a) $4 \div \frac{1}{5}$

(b) $1 \div \frac{1}{10}$

(c) $3 \div \frac{1}{12}$

(d) $50 \div \frac{1}{2}$

6 (a) $3 \div \boxed{\dfrac{1}{}} = 6$

(b) $7 \div \boxed{\dfrac{1}{}} = 28$

(c) $\boxed{} \div \dfrac{1}{4} = 40$

(d) $\boxed{} \div \dfrac{1}{6} = 54$

7 Each of the sides of a polygon is $\dfrac{1}{5}$ m long. The perimeter of the polygon is 2 m. How many sides does the polygon have?

8 $\dfrac{1}{12}$ of a length of rope is 5 ft. How long is the rope in feet?

Basics

1 How many $\frac{2}{5}$s are in 2 wholes?

$2 \div \frac{1}{5} = 2 \times 5$

$2 \div \frac{2}{5} = \frac{2 \times 5}{2}$

$= 2 \times \boxed{\dfrac{}{2}}$

$= \boxed{}$

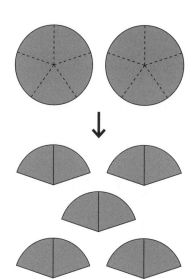

2 (a) _____ is the reciprocal of $\frac{2}{3}$.

(b) How many $\frac{2}{3}$s are in 6?

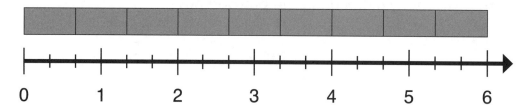

$6 \div \frac{2}{3} = 6 \times \frac{3}{2} = \boxed{}$

(c) How many $\frac{2}{3}$s are in 3?

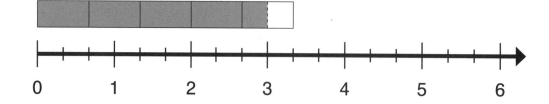

$3 \div \frac{2}{3} = 3 \times \frac{3}{2} = \boxed{\dfrac{}{2}} = \boxed{}\boxed{\dfrac{}{}}$

3 (a) _____ is the reciprocal of $\frac{3}{5}$.

(b) $\frac{3}{5}$ of what number is 3?

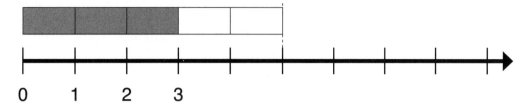

$3 \div \frac{3}{5} = 3 \times \boxed{\dfrac{}{3}} = \boxed{}$

(c) $\frac{3}{5}$ of what number is 5?

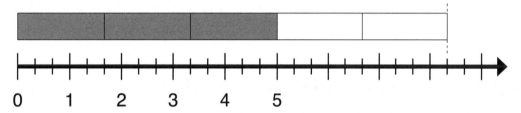

$5 \div \frac{3}{5} = 5 \times \boxed{\dfrac{}{3}} = \boxed{\dfrac{}{3}} = \boxed{}\,\boxed{\dfrac{}{}}$

Practice

4 Divide.

(a) $3 \div \frac{3}{10}$ (b) $4 \div \frac{2}{5}$

(c) $6 \div \frac{3}{7}$ (d) $60 \div \frac{4}{5}$

5 Divide. Express each answer in simplest form.

(a) $7 \div \frac{2}{3}$

(b) $8 \div \frac{3}{4}$

(c) $6 \div \frac{4}{3}$

(d) $60 \div \frac{9}{5}$

6 A sheet of plywood is $\frac{3}{8}$ inches thick. A stack of these sheets of plywood is 9 inches high. How many sheets of plywood are in the stack?

7 Crushed garlic is divided into small containers to be frozen and used later. One of the containers has 5 g of crushed garlic, which is $\frac{2}{7}$ of the total amount of crushed garlic. What is the weight of the total amount of crushed garlic?

Basics

1 A farmer had 100 lb of brussels sprouts. He put them into bags each holding $\frac{2}{3}$ lb to sell at the farmer's market. He then sold $\frac{3}{5}$ of the bags in the morning and $\frac{7}{10}$ of the remaining bags in the afternoon.

(a) How many bags of brussels sprouts did he have?

$100 \div \frac{2}{3} =$

(b) What fraction of the brussels sprouts did he sell in the afternoon?

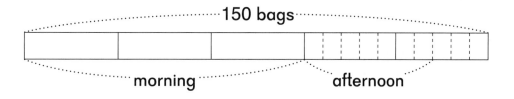

$\frac{7}{10} \times \frac{2}{5} =$

(c) How many pounds of brussels sprouts does he have left?

Practice

2 A box with 8 bags of pretzels and a jar of mustard weighs $2\frac{1}{6}$ lb. The jar of mustard weighs $1\frac{3}{8}$ lb and the box weighs $\frac{1}{8}$ lb. 5 bags of pretzels were taken out. How many pounds does the box with the remaining bags and jar of mustard now weigh?

3 A farm harvested 432 lb of cherries. It sold $\frac{5}{9}$ of the cherries to stores and put $\frac{5}{8}$ of the remainder into bags holding $\frac{3}{4}$ lb, which it sold at a stand for $4 each. How much money did the farm receive from the sales at the stand?

4 Trees are going to be planted along the side of a road. One tree will be planted at the start, then another 30 trees for $\frac{3}{5}$ km total. The remaining stretch of the road will have an additional 25 trees in all planted every $\frac{1}{10}$ km.

(a) How many kilometers apart from each other will the first 31 trees be?

(b) How long is the road in kilometers?

5 A store sold 12 laptops on Saturday and $\frac{2}{5}$ of its remaining laptops on Sunday. Altogether the store sold $\frac{2}{3}$ of its stock of laptops in those two days. How many laptops did it have at first?

Exercise 7

Check

1 Find the values. Express each answer in simplest form.

(a) $5 \div \frac{1}{6}$

(b) $7 \div \frac{1}{8}$

(c) $6 \div \frac{3}{4}$

(d) $12 \div \frac{2}{3}$

(e) $100 \div \frac{4}{5}$

(f) $5 \div \frac{5}{6}$

(g) $4 \div \frac{8}{9}$

(h) $100 \div \frac{6}{7}$

(i) $10 \div \frac{2}{3} \times \frac{1}{2}$

(j) $\left(2\frac{1}{7} \times 2\frac{1}{3}\right) \div \frac{7}{10}$

(k) $35 \div \frac{2}{3} - 17 \div \frac{2}{3}$

(l) $25 \div \frac{1}{2} - 25 \div \frac{2}{3}$

2 A sheet of plywood is $\frac{3}{4}$ in thick. A stack of these sheets of plywood is 2 feet high. How many sheets of plywood are in the stack?

3 Mariam is cutting 20 inches of yarn into pieces each $\frac{3}{8}$ inch long for an art project. How many $\frac{3}{8}$ inch pieces will she have?

4 One lap around a track is $\frac{1}{3}$ of a mile. Riya ran 5 miles around the track. How many laps did she run?

5 A store made 96 lb of peppermint bark for the holidays. The peppermint bark was split into $\frac{3}{8}$ lb portions and boxed. $\frac{3}{4}$ of the boxes were sold for $6 each before the holidays. The rest were sold at $\frac{2}{3}$ of the pre-holiday price. How much money did the shop receive from the sales of the peppermint bark?

6 Ray used 45 bags of cement to build a patio. Each bag of cement contained 95 lb of cement. The patio is $\frac{3}{8}$ the area of a driveway that he is going to build. How many 95 lb bags of cement does he need to build the driveway?

Challenge

7 A tank was $\frac{1}{4}$ of the way filled of water. After 3 L of water was added, it was $\frac{7}{10}$ full. How many liters of water did it have at first?

8 A jug was $\frac{1}{4}$ full of water. After some water was added, it was $\frac{7}{10}$ full. It is now $\frac{1}{2}$ L from being full. How many liters of water were added?

9 One small block is $\frac{2}{3}$ of the weight of a large block. How many of the available blocks need to be added to the right side so that it is balanced?

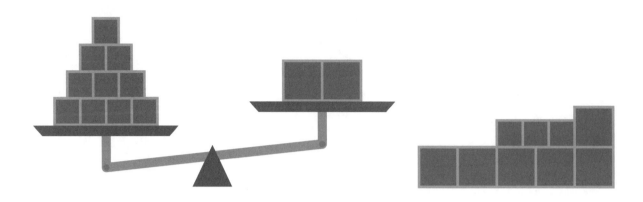

10 It would take Steve 4 hours to paint a room. If Andre helps him, they can finish painting the room in 3 hours. How long would Andre take to paint the room by himself?

Chapter 7 Measurement

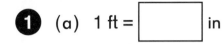

Basics

1 (a) 1 ft = ⬚ in   (b) 1 lb = ⬚ oz

(c) 1 yd = ⬚ ft   (d) 1 qt = ⬚ c

(e) 1 gal = ⬚ qt   (f) 1 day = ⬚ h

(g) 1 h = ⬚ min   (h) 1 min = ⬚ s

(i) 1 km = ⬚ m   (j) 1 L = ⬚ mL

(k) 1 kg = ⬚ g   (l) 1 m = ⬚ cm

(m) 1 cm = ⬚ mm   (n) 1 L = ⬚ dL

2 (a) $3 \text{ L} = 3 \times$ ⬚ $\text{mL} = 3{,}000 \text{ mL}$

(b) $\frac{3}{8} \text{ L} = \frac{3}{8} \times$ ⬚ $\text{mL} =$ ⬚ mL

(c) $3\frac{3}{8} \text{ L} =$ ⬚ $\text{mL} +$ ⬚ $\text{mL} =$ ⬚ mL

3 Express $7\frac{3}{4}$ ft in inches.

$7 \times 12 + \frac{3}{4} \times 12 = 84 +$ ⬚ $=$ ⬚

$7\frac{3}{4}$ ft = ⬚ in

Practice

 (a) $4\frac{3}{10}$ km = ☐ km ☐ m

(b) $2\frac{3}{4}$ lb = ☐ lb ☐ oz

(c) $6\frac{3}{5}$ cm = ☐ cm ☐ mm

5 **(a)** $2\frac{3}{8}$ lb = ☐ oz   **(b)** $3\frac{4}{5}$ min = ☐ s

(c) $6\frac{3}{5}$ km = ☐ m   **(d)** $5\frac{3}{20}$ m = ☐ cm

(e) $4\frac{1}{2}$ gal = ☐ qt   **(f)** $5\frac{2}{3}$ yd = ☐ ft

(g) $2\frac{3}{4}$ kg = ☐ g   **(h)** $2\frac{1}{2}$ days = ☐ h

6 A bag of beans weighs $2\frac{1}{2}$ lb. 12 ounces of beans were used for soup, and another $1\frac{1}{8}$ lb of beans were used to make chili. How many ounces of beans are still in the bag?

7 In a 2 h practice, a team spent 10 min on warm up, and $1\frac{2}{3}$ h on drills. How many minutes are left for stretching at the end?

8 A fathom is 6 ft. The sonar says that a submarine is at a depth of $18\frac{2}{3}$ fathoms. How many feet deep is the submarine?

9 1 mile is 5,280 ft. How many yards are in $\frac{3}{4}$ miles?

Basics

1 What is the area of a rectangle that is $\frac{3}{4}$ ft long and $\frac{2}{3}$ ft wide in square feet?

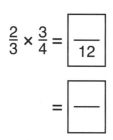

$\frac{2}{3} \times \frac{3}{4} = \boxed{\dfrac{}{12}}$

$= \boxed{\dfrac{}{}}$

Area $= \frac{1}{2}$ ft²

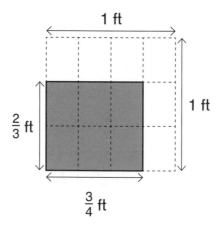

1 ft

1 ft

$\frac{2}{3}$ ft

$\frac{3}{4}$ ft

2 What is the area of a rectangle that is $2\frac{1}{5}$ m long and $1\frac{1}{2}$ m wide in square meters?

$2\frac{1}{5} \times 1\frac{1}{2} = \boxed{\dfrac{}{5}} \times \boxed{\dfrac{}{2}}$

$= \boxed{\dfrac{}{}}$

$= \boxed{}\boxed{\dfrac{}{}}$

Area $= 3\frac{3}{10}$ m²

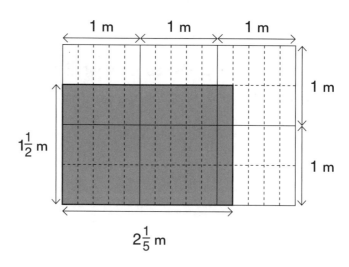

1 m   1 m   1 m

1 m

1 m

$1\frac{1}{2}$ m

$2\frac{1}{5}$ m

3 What is the area of a rectangle that is 4 in long and $2\frac{3}{8}$ in wide?

$4 \times 2\frac{3}{8} = 4 \times \boxed{\dfrac{}{8}} = \boxed{\dfrac{}{}} = \boxed{}\boxed{\dfrac{}{}}$

Area $= 9\frac{1}{2}$ in²

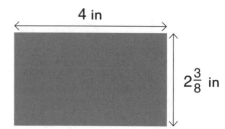

4 in

$2\frac{3}{8}$ in

Practice

4 Find the area of each figure.

(a)

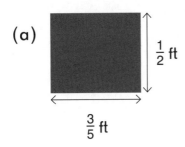

$\frac{1}{2}$ ft

$\frac{3}{5}$ ft

(b)

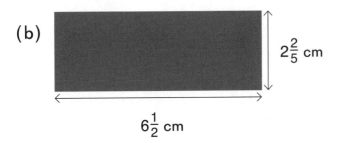

$2\frac{2}{5}$ cm

$6\frac{1}{2}$ cm

(c)

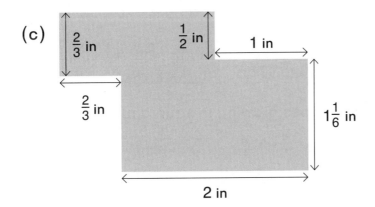

$\frac{2}{3}$ in

$\frac{1}{2}$ in

1 in

$\frac{2}{3}$ in

$1\frac{1}{6}$ in

2 in

5 The figure is made up of 3 identical rectangles. What is the area of the figure?

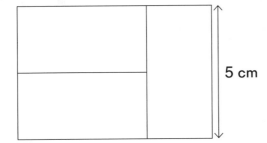

5 cm

6 A gravel path, $1\frac{1}{2}$ m wide, surrounds a grass lawn, $18\frac{1}{2}$ m by 11 m. A garden shed in the middle of the lawn is 5 m by $3\frac{1}{4}$ m.

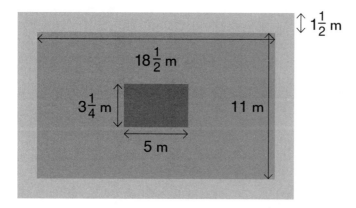

(a) What is the area of the path in square meters?

(b) What is the area that has grass growing in square meters?

7 Aiden is painting a rectangular wall that is $15\frac{1}{5}$ ft by $12\frac{1}{2}$ ft. He needs 1 quart of paint for every 60 square feet of wall. How many 1-quart cans does he need to buy?

Check

1 Anthony's cat slept for $\frac{2}{3}$ of the time between 6:00 a.m. one morning to 6:00 a.m. the next morning. How many hours did it sleep?

2 Tyler read for $1\frac{2}{3}$ h in the afternoon and $\frac{3}{4}$ h before bed. How many minutes did he spend reading that day?

3 Diego's time for a 100-m sprint was $\frac{3}{5}$ min. Adam took $\frac{5}{6}$ as long as Diego to complete the same sprint. How many seconds did Adam take to sprint 100 meters?

4 The area of a rectangle is 2 ft². One side is $\frac{3}{4}$ ft long. What is the length of the other side in inches?

5 A recipe calls for $\frac{2}{3}$ of a stick of butter. Natasha wants to double the recipe. 4 sticks of butter weigh 1 pound. How many ounces of butter will she use?

6 A rectangle is $2\frac{1}{6}$ ft long and $1\frac{2}{3}$ ft wide.

(a) What is its area in square feet?

(b) What is its area in square inches?

Challenge

7 When four identical right triangles are arranged as follows, a square inside a square is formed. What is the area of the shaded part of the figure in square inches?

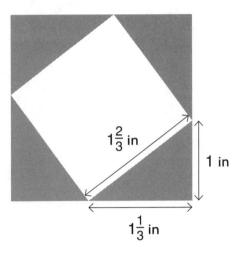

$1\frac{2}{3}$ in

1 in

$1\frac{1}{3}$ in

8 In medieval times, a "moment" was $\frac{1}{10}$ of a "point." A point was 15 minutes.

(a) How many minutes is a moment?

(b) How many seconds is a moment?

Basics

1 Find the area of each triangle. Each square represents 1 cm².

(a)

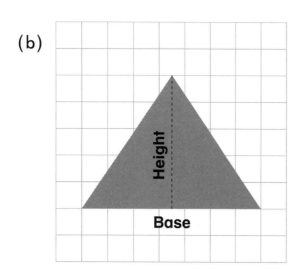

Area = $\frac{1}{2}$ × base × height

= $\frac{1}{2}$ × 8 × 6

= ☐ cm²

(b)

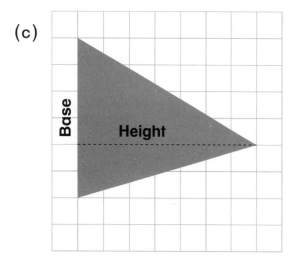

Area = $\frac{1}{2}$ × 7 × 5

= $\dfrac{\boxed{}}{2}$

= ☐ $\boxed{\dfrac{}{}}$ cm²

(c)

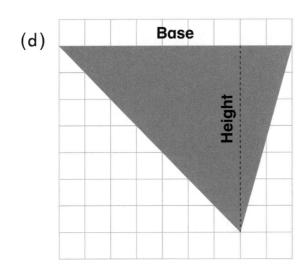

(d)

2 For each triangle, identify a base (if required) and a corresponding height.

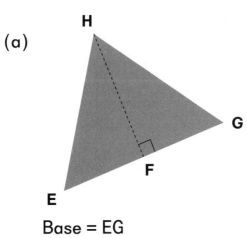

(a)

Base = EG

Height =

(b)

Base = MK

Height =

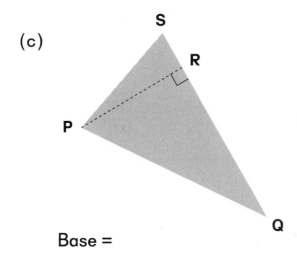

(c)

Base =

Height =

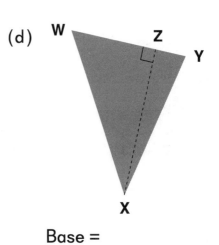

(d)

Base =

Height =

Practice

3 Draw a height for the given base of each of these triangles.

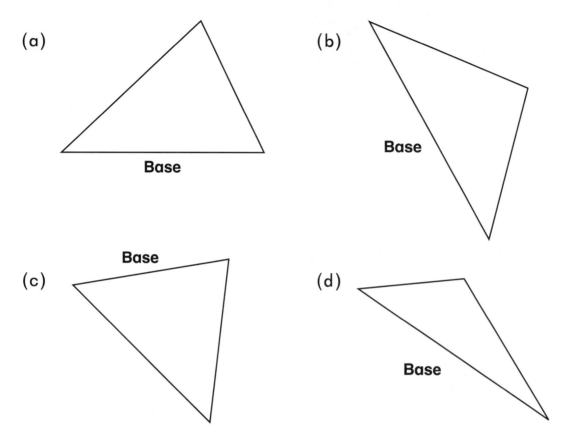

(a)

Base

(b)

Base

(c)

Base

(d)

Base

4 Find the area of each shaded triangle.

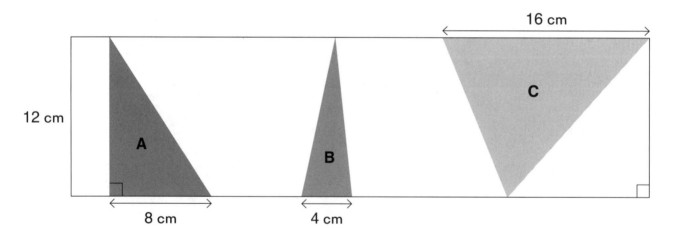

16 cm

12 cm

A

B

C

8 cm

4 cm

5 Find the area of each triangle.

(a)

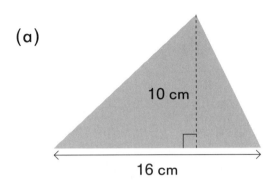

10 cm

16 cm

(b)

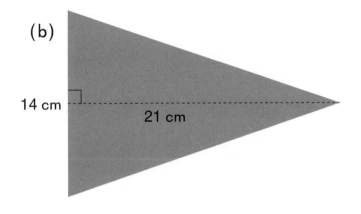

14 cm

21 cm

(c)

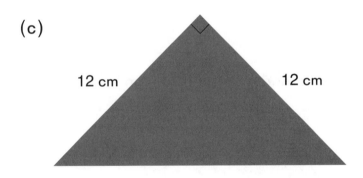

12 cm   12 cm

(d)

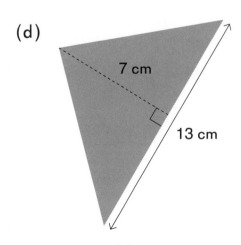

7 cm

13 cm

6 Find the area of each triangle.

(a)

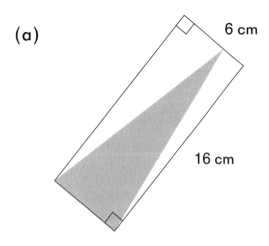

6 cm

16 cm

(b)

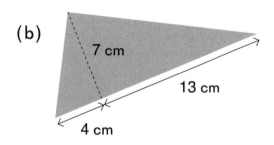

7 cm

13 cm

4 cm

Challenge

7 (a) A triangle has a base of 5 cm and an area of 20 cm². What is its height?

(b) A triangle has a height of 3 cm and an area of $7\frac{1}{2}$ cm². What is its base?

Basics

1 Find the area of each triangle. Each square represents 1 cm².

(a)

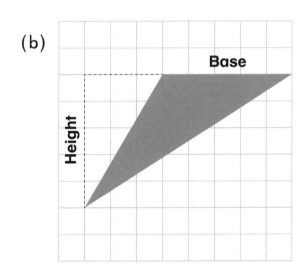

Area = $\frac{1}{2}$ × base × height

= $\frac{1}{2}$ × 6 × 7

= ☐ cm²

(b)

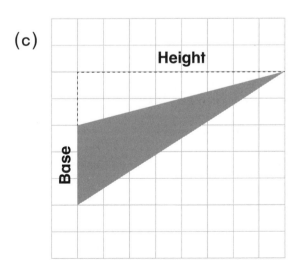

Area = $\frac{1}{2}$ × 5 × 5

= $\dfrac{}{2}$

= ☐ $\dfrac{}{}$ cm²

(c)

2 For each triangle, identify a base for the given height.

(a)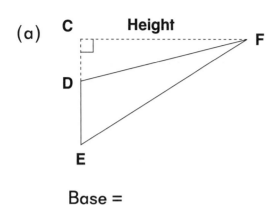

Base = _____

(b)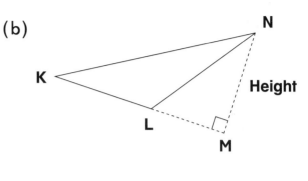

Base = _____

Practice

3 Draw a height for the given base of each of these triangles.

(a)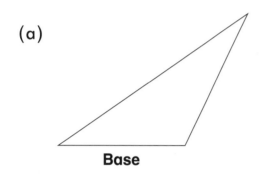

(b)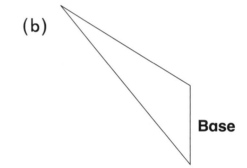

4 Identify the height of each given base.

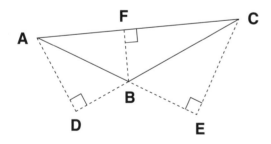

If the base is AB, the height is _____.

If the base is BC, the height is _____.

If the base is CA, the height is _____.

5 Find the area of each triangle.

(a)

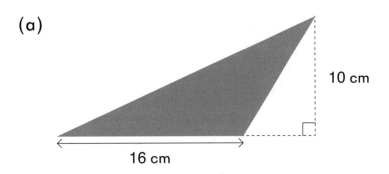
10 cm
16 cm

(b)

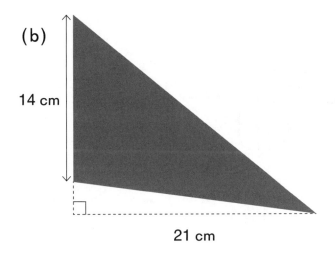
14 cm
21 cm

(c)

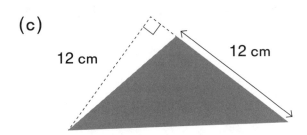
12 cm
12 cm

(d)

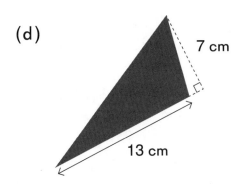
7 cm
13 cm

6 Find the area of each shaded triangle.

(a)

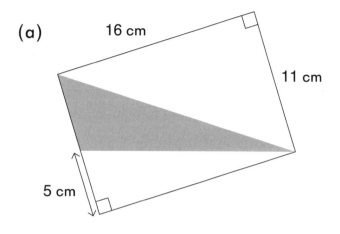

16 cm

11 cm

5 cm

(b)

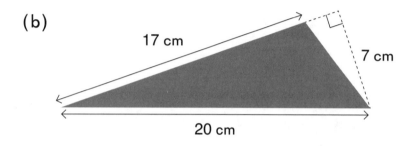

17 cm

7 cm

20 cm

Challenge

7 In the following figure, AC = 24 cm, BC = 12 cm, and AE = 16 cm. Find the length of BD.

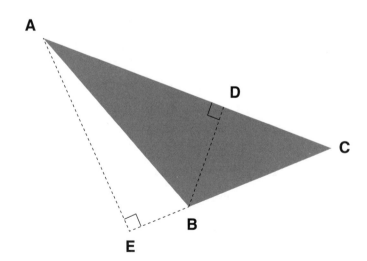

A

D

C

B

E

Basics

1 Find the area of the shaded figures. Each square represents 1 cm².

(a)

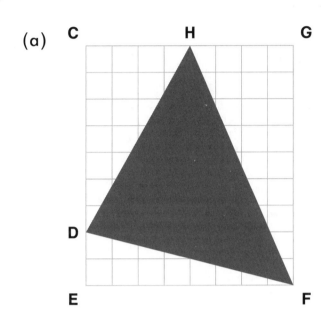

Area of Rectangle CEFG:

Area of Triangle CDH:

Area of Triangle DEF:

Area of Triangle HFG:

Area of Triangle HDF:

(b)

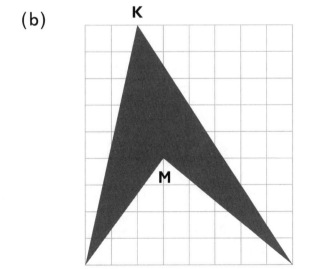

Area of Triangle LKN:

Area of Triangle LMN:

Area of Figure KLMN:

2 Find the area of the shaded figure.

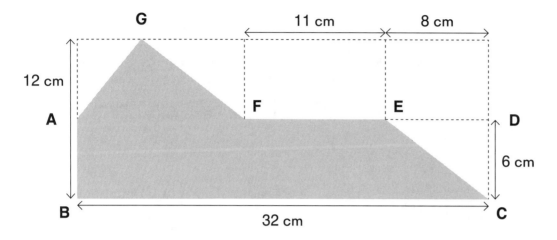

Area of Rectangle ABCD:

Area of Triangle AFG:

Area of Triangle CDE:

Area of Figure ABCEFG:

3 The figure below is made up of two squares, ABCG and FCDE. Find the area of the shaded part.

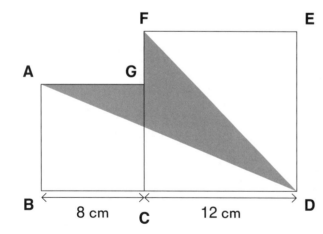

Area of Triangle ABD:

Area of Triangle FDE:

Area of both squares:

Area of Figure ADFG:

Practice

4 Find the area of the shaded figure. Each square represents 1 cm².

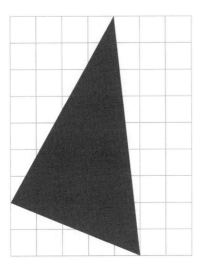

5 Find the area of the shaded figure.

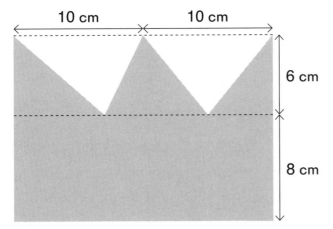

6 4 identical triangles are cut from the corners of a rectangular paper that is 20 cm long and 12 cm wide. What is the area of the paper left?

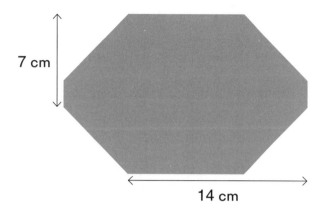

7 cm

14 cm

7 The figure below shows two squares. Find the area of the shaded triangle.

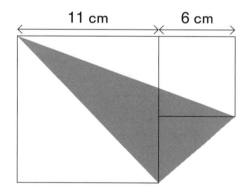

11 cm   6 cm

Challenge

8 Find the area of the shaded figure.

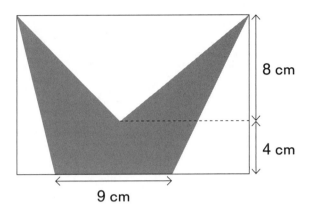

8 cm

4 cm

9 cm

9 What is the area of the triangle shown below?

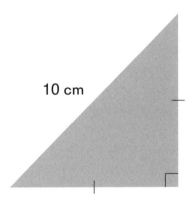

10 cm

Exercise 7

Check

1 Find the area of each triangle.

(a)
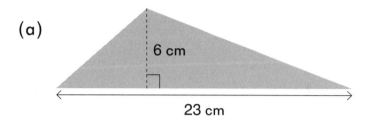

(b)
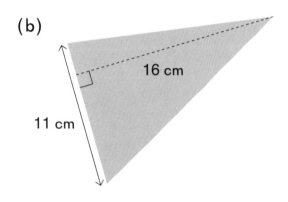

(c)
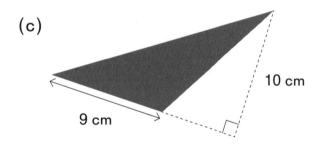

(d)
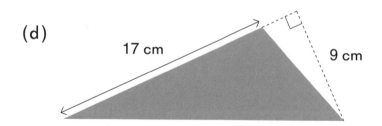

2 Find the shaded areas. Each square represents 1 cm².

(a)

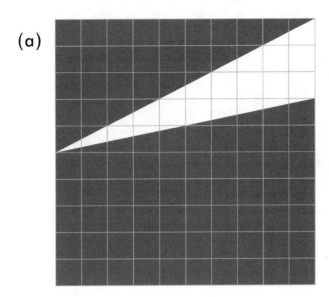

(b)

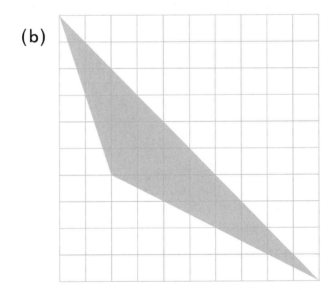

3 The figure is made from a rectangle and 2 identical right triangles. Find the area.

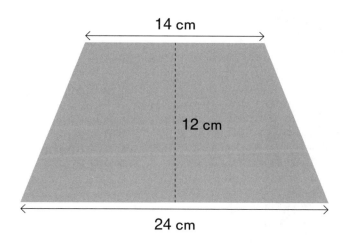

14 cm

12 cm

24 cm

4 The figure is made from a square and two identical triangles. Find the area.

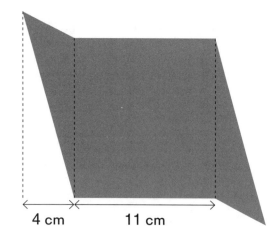

4 cm   11 cm

5 The figure is made from two squares and a right triangle. The areas of the two squares are 64 cm² and 36 cm². What is the area of the triangle?

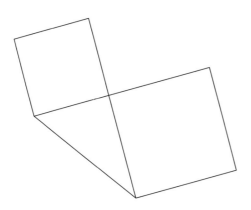

6 The area of Triangle ADE is $\frac{1}{3}$ the area of Triangle ABC. Find the shaded area.

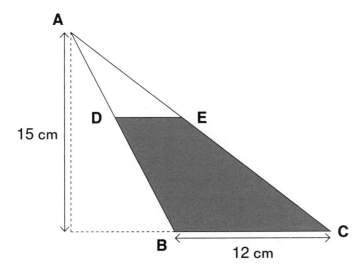

Challenge

7 The figure below shows three squares. Find the area of the shaded part.

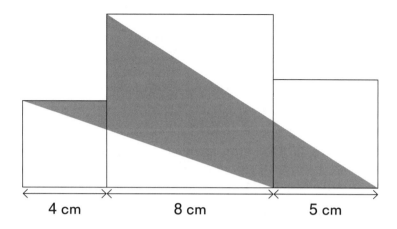

| 4 cm | 8 cm | 5 cm |

8 The area of triangle ABC is 3 times the area of Triangle ABD. Triangle DBE is an isosceles right triangle. Find the area of Triangle DBE.

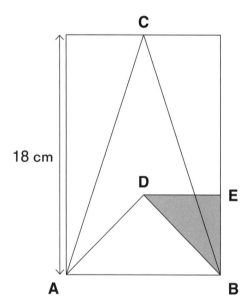

Chapter 8 Volume of Solid Figures

Basics

1 A cube that is 1 cm on each side has a volume of
_____ cubic centimeter, which is written as _____ cm³.

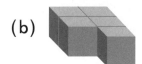

2 The following solid figures were made using 1-cm cubes. Find the volumes.

(a)

(b)

(c)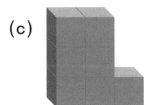

(d)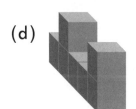

3 _____ cubes are needed to build this solid.
One cube is hidden under a top block.

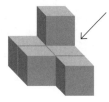

4 Find the volumes of the following solid figures, which were made using
1-cm cubes.

(a)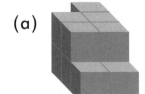

(b)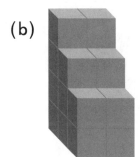

5 The following solid figures were made using 1-inch cubes. Find the volumes.

(a)

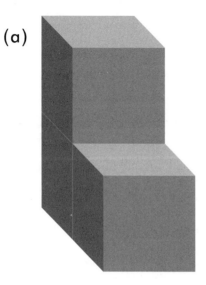

(b)

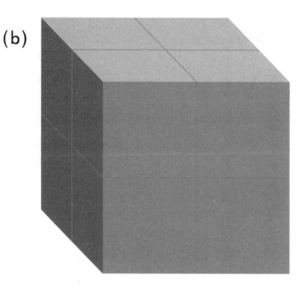

Practice

6 The following solid figures were made using 1-cm cubes. Find the volumes.

(a)

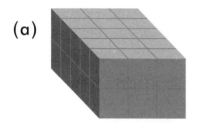

(b)

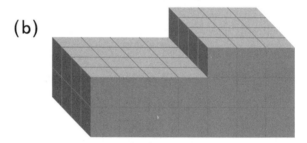

(c)

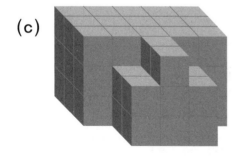

(d)

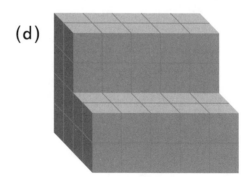

7 How many cubes were added to or removed from the solid on the left to create the solid on the right?

(a)

(b)

(c)

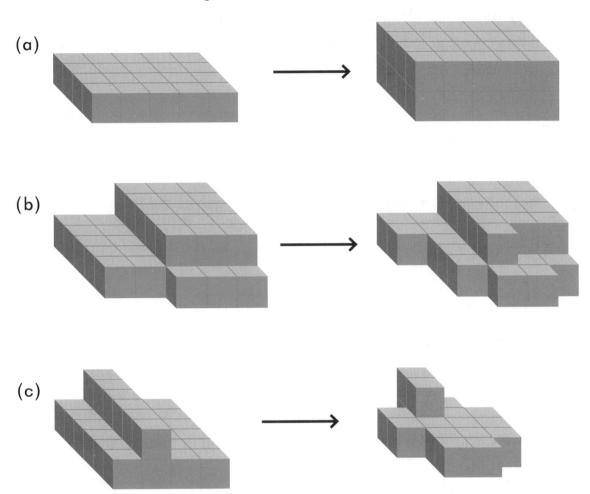

8 How many unit cubes need to be added to each figure to make a larger cube that has a length, width, and height each of 4 units?

(a)   (b)

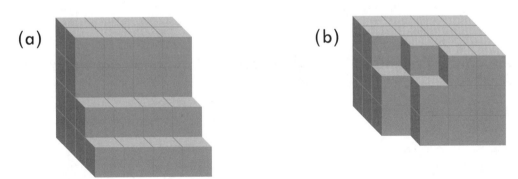

Challenge

The following shows some different ways cubes can be drawn using dot grids. The two cubes on the left each have a face facing forward, whereas the cube on the right has an edge facing forward.

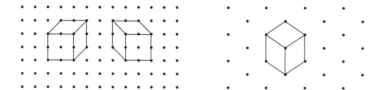

9 How many unit cubes are needed to build each of the following figures?

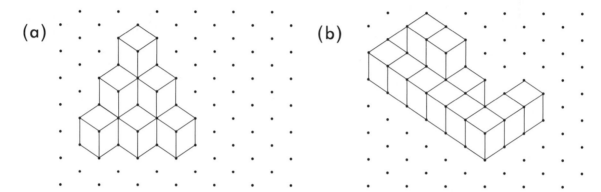

(a)

(b)

10 Draw the figure that you will see when one unit cube is added to each of the shaded faces.

11 Draw the figure that you will see when the shaded cubes are removed.

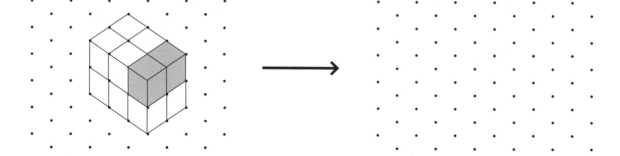

Basics

1 Find the volume of the solid figures. Each was made using 1-cm cubes.

(a)

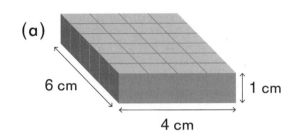

6 cm 1 cm 4 cm

4 × 6 × 1 = ☐

Volume = ☐ cm³

(b)

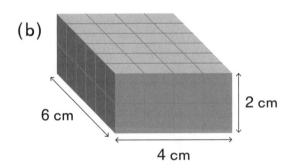

6 cm 2 cm 4 cm

4 × 6 × 2 = ☐

Volume = ☐ cm³

(c)

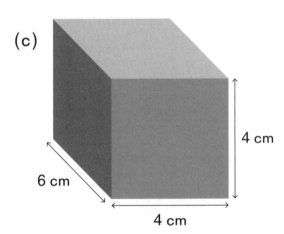

6 cm 4 cm 4 cm

4 × ☐ × ☐ = ☐

Volume = ☐ cm³

(d)

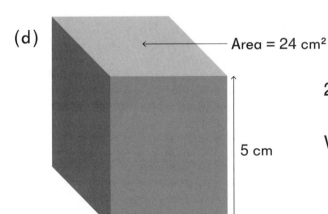

Area = 24 cm²

5 cm

24 × 5 = ☐

Volume = ☐ cm³

Practice

2 Find the volume of each cuboid.

(a)

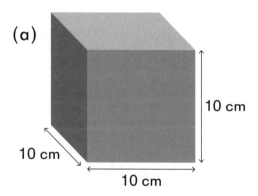

10 cm

10 cm

10 cm

(b)

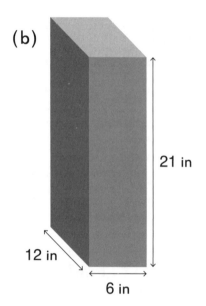

21 in

12 in

6 in

(c)

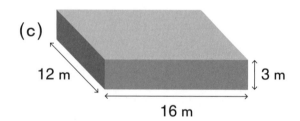

12 m

3 m

16 m

(d)

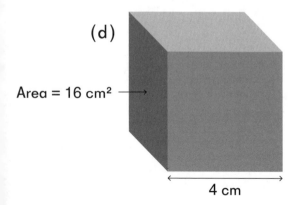

Area = 16 cm² →

4 cm

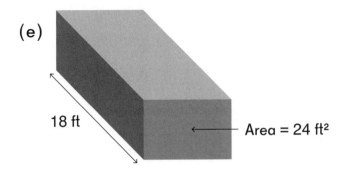

(e)

18 ft

Area = 24 ft²

3 What is the difference in volume between these two cuboids?

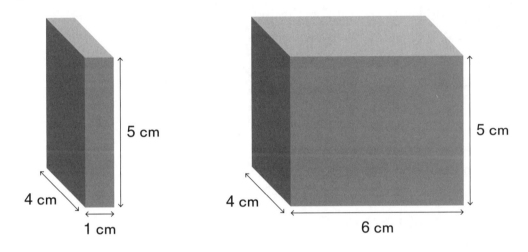

5 cm

4 cm

1 cm

5 cm

4 cm

6 cm

4 A cube is 9 cm long on each side. A cuboid is 9 cm by 8 cm by 10 cm. Which solid has a greater volume, and by how much?

Challenge

5 A crate has the dimensions of 24 inches by 16 inches by 12 inches. How many 2-inch cubes can it hold?

Basics

1 The volume of this cuboid is 96 cm³. The bottom face is 6 cm by 4 cm. What is the height of the cuboid?

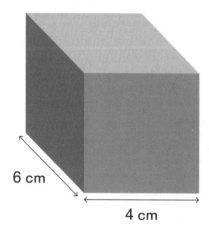 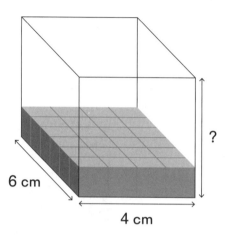

6 cm

4 cm

6 cm

4 cm

?

Number of 1-cm cubes in the bottom layer: 6 × 4

Number of layers of cubes: $96 \div (6 \times 4) = \frac{96}{6 \times 4} = $ ☐

Height = ☐ cm

2 The volume of this cuboid is 432 cm³. Its height is 6 cm and its length is 12 cm. What is the width of the cuboid?

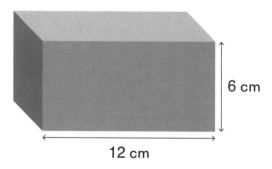

6 cm

12 cm

12 × 6 × Width = 432

Width = $\frac{432}{12 \times 6} = $ ☐

Width = ☐ cm

3 The volume of a cuboid is 84 cm³. The top face has an area of 28 cm².
What is the height of the cuboid?

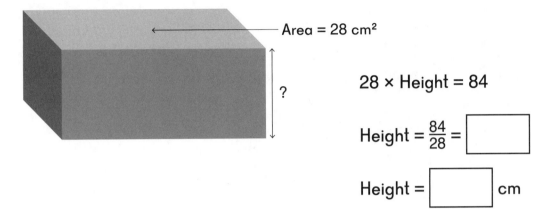

Area = 28 cm²

?

28 × Height = 84

Height = $\frac{84}{28}$ = ☐

Height = ☐ cm

Practice

4 Find the length of the unknown edge of each cuboid.

(a) Volume = 600 cm³

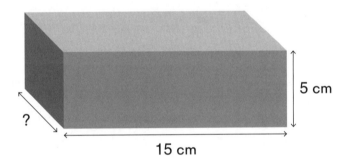

5 cm

?

15 cm

(b) Volume = 352 in³

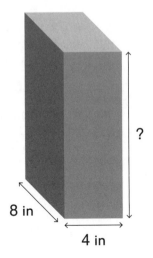

?

8 in

4 in

(c) Volume = 252 m³

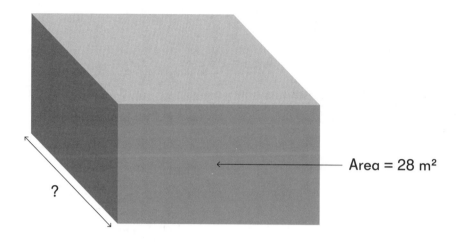

Area = 28 m²

?

(d) Volume = 540 cm³

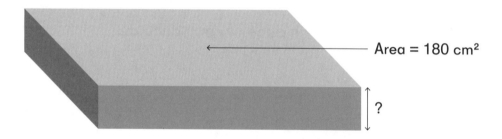

Area = 180 cm²

?

5 A shipping container is 20 ft long and 8 ft wide with a volume of 1,360 ft³. How high is it in feet?

Challenge

6 A rectangular container has a volume of 468 cm³. The base is a square with an area of 36 cm². How many 2-cm cubes can fit in the container?

Check

1 The following solid figures were made using 1-cm cubes. Find the volumes.

(a)

(b)

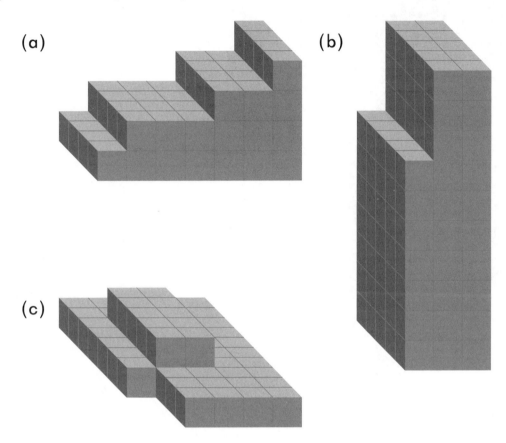

(c)

2 How many cubes need to be added to the figure below to make a cuboid with a base area of 30 square units and a height of 4 units?

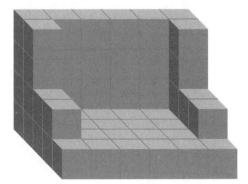

3 Find the volume of each cuboid.

(a)

11 cm

11 cm

20 cm

(b)

11 cm

Area = 192 cm²

4 Find the length of the unknown edge of each cuboid.

(a) Volume = 2,100 cm³

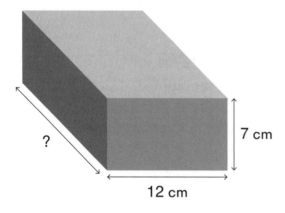

?

7 cm

12 cm

(b) Volume = 1,920 cm³

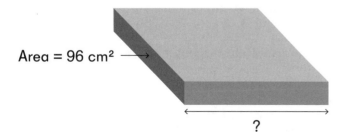

Area = 96 cm²

?

5 The base of a crate has an area of 1,200 ft². The volume of the crate is 30,000 ft³. What is its height?

6 A solid is made up of 8 cubes each with an edge of 4 cm. What is the volume of the solid?

7 Each layer of a structure forms a square. The bottom layer has 100 1-cm cubes. The next layer up has 81 cubes, and the next layer up has 64 cubes. This pattern continues until the top layer has 16 cubes.

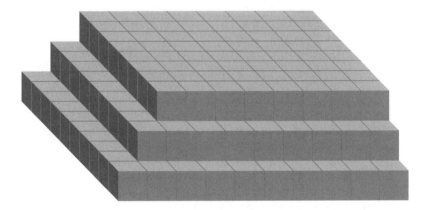

(a) What is the volume of the entire structure?

(b) How many more cubes need to be added to have a larger cube with sides 10 cm long?

Challenge

8 3 metal cubes are 3 cm, 4 cm, and 5 cm long. They were melted and recast into one new cube. What is the length of the new cube?

9 How many 2-cm cubes can be put in a rectangular container measuring 20 cm by 15 cm by 12 cm?

10 Twenty-four 4-cm cubes are used to make a solid. If 2-cm cubes were used instead, how many cubes would be needed?

Basics

1 A block with a width of 6 cm, a length of 9 cm, and a height of 7 cm is placed on top of another block with the same width, but with a length of 15 cm and a height of 5 cm. What is the volume of the structure?

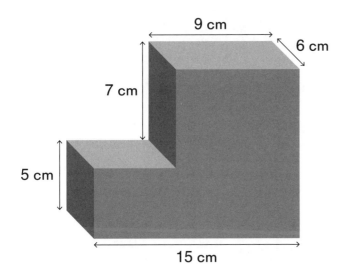

$9 \times 6 \times 7 =$ ▢

$15 \times 6 \times 5 =$ ▢

▢ $+$ ▢ $=$ ▢

Volume $=$ ▢ cm³

2 Two cubes with lengths of 5 cm are cut from a cuboid that is 12 cm by 5 cm by 15 cm. What is the volume of the remaining solid?

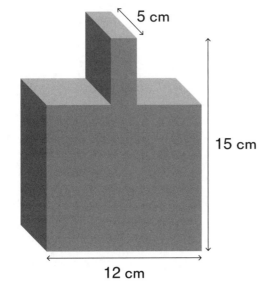

$12 \times 5 \times 15 =$ ▢

$2 \times (5 \times 5 \times 5) =$ ▢

▢ $-$ ▢ $=$ ▢

Volume $=$ ▢ cm³

Practice

3 Find the volume of each solid figure.

(a)

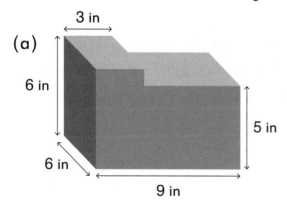

3 in

6 in

6 in

9 in

5 in

(b)

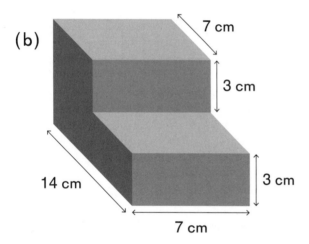

7 cm

3 cm

3 cm

14 cm

7 cm

(c)

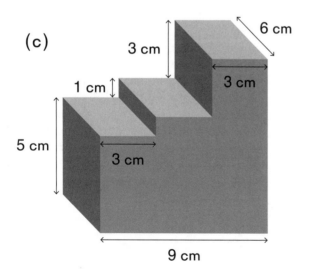

6 cm

3 cm

3 cm

1 cm

5 cm

3 cm

9 cm

(d)

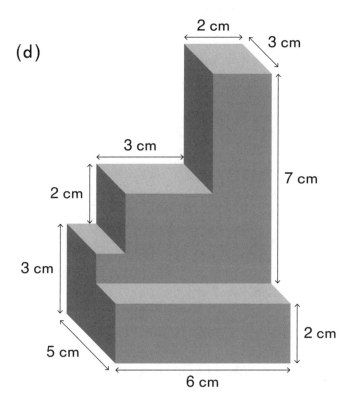

4 A cuboid has a cuboid hole in it. The front and back faces of the hole are squares. Find the volume of the remaining solid.

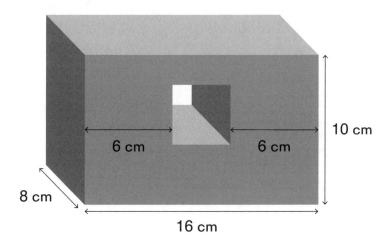

Basics

1

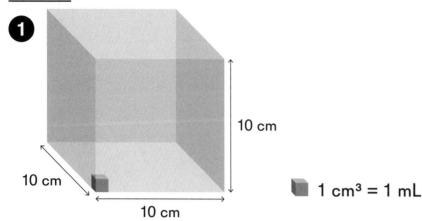

10 cm

10 cm

10 cm

1 cm³ = 1 mL

(a) What is the volume of this tank in cubic centimeters?

(b) What is its capacity in milliliters?

(c) What is its capacity in liters?

2 (a) 40 cm³ = [   ] mL

(b) 400 cm³ = [   ] mL

(c) 4,000 cm³ = [   ] mL = [   ] L

(d) 4,030 cm³ = [   ] mL = [   ] L [   ] mL

(e) 850 mL = [   ] cm³

(f) 1 L 850 mL = [   ] mL = [   ] cm³

(g) 1 L 85 mL = [   ] mL = [   ] cm³

3 A rectangular tank is partially filled with water to a depth of 8 cm. Find the volume of water in the tank in liters and milliliters.

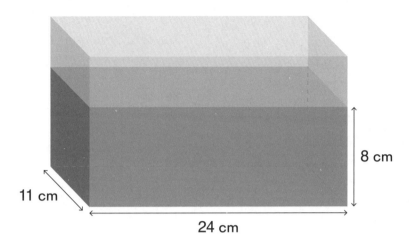

24 × 11 × 8 = ☐

Volume = ☐ cm³

Volume = ☐ L ☐ mL

Practice

4 A rectangular container, 20 cm long and 10 cm wide, contains 1 L 400 mL of water. What is the height of the water?

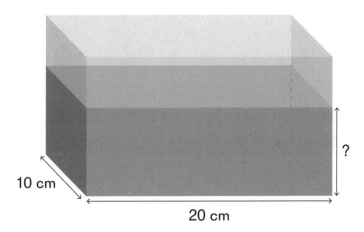

5 A rectangular container, 20 cm by 30 cm by 42 cm, is filled completely with water. 18 L of water is then poured out. What is the height of the water left in the container?

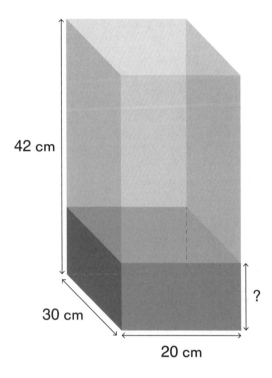

42 cm

30 cm

20 cm

?

6 A rectangular tank 15 cm long, 10 cm wide, and 40 cm high is $\frac{4}{5}$ full of water. How many more liters and milliliters of water are needed to fill the tank completely?

7 A bottle containing 2 L of water is poured into a rectangular tank with a base area of 240 cm² and a height of 12 cm until the tank is $\frac{2}{3}$ full. How much water is left in the bottle?

Basics

1 A rectangular tank with a base area of 30 cm by 20 cm is filled with water to a height of 12 cm.

(a) An object is placed in the tank and the water rises to 15 cm. What is the volume of the object?

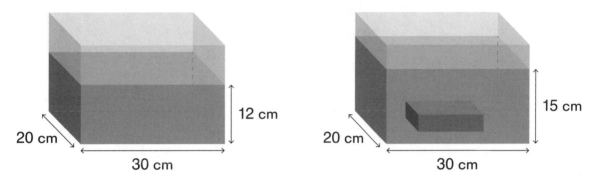

Increase in height of water level = 15 − 12 = ▢

Volume of water displaced = 30 × 20 × ▢ = ▢

Volume of object = ▢ cm³

(b) Another object with a volume of 1,200 cm³ is added to the tank. What will be the new height of the water?

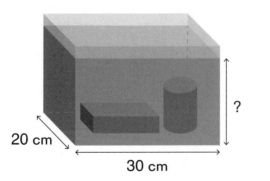

$\dfrac{1{,}200}{20 \times 30}$ = ▢

15 + ▢ = ▢

New height of water = ▢ cm

Practice

2 A measuring cylinder had 500 mL of water in it. After 20 identical glass marbles were added, the water level was 840 mL.

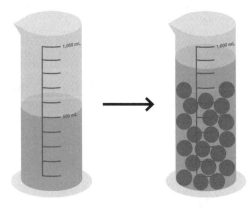

(a) What is the volume of the 20 marbles?

(b) What is the volume of a single marble?

3 A cubical container with sides of 30 cm was $\frac{2}{3}$ filled with water. After an object was placed in it, the water level rose to 4 cm from the top. What is the volume of the object?

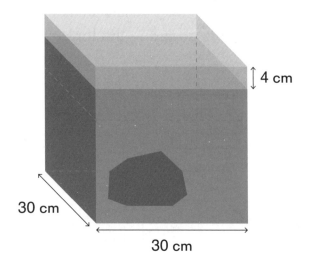

4 cm

30 cm

30 cm

4 William put water in a rectangular tank and then added identical game tokens until the water rose by 2 cm. The base of the tank measures 10 cm by 8 cm. He added 12 game tokens in all. What is the volume of 1 game token?

5 A rectangular container, 30 cm long and 10 cm wide, contains 2 L 400 mL of water. Two identical cuboids with the dimensions of 10 cm by 3 cm by 5 cm are in the water. What is the height of the water?

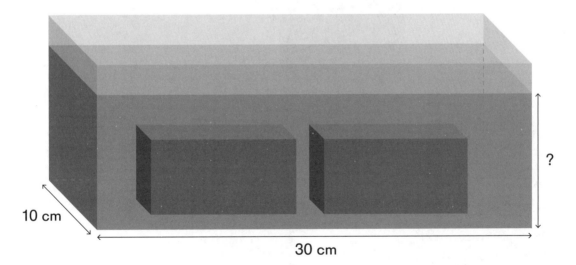

10 cm

30 cm

?

Check

1 Find the volume of each solid figure.

(a)

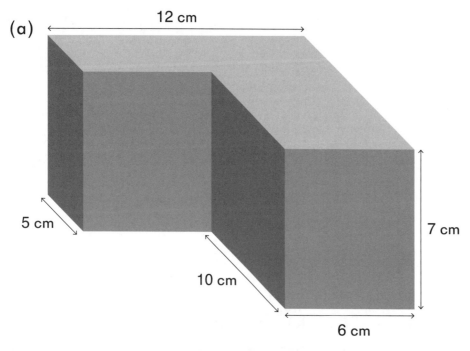

(b)

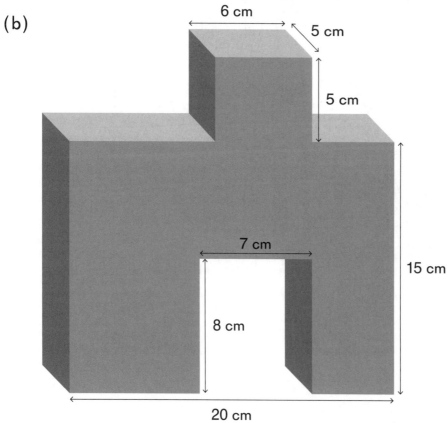

2 (a) 64 cm³ = [　　　] mL

(b) 3,420 cm³ = [　　　] L [　　　] mL

(c) 6,007 cm³ = [　　　] L [　　　] mL

(d) 98 mL = [　　　] cm³

(e) 6 L = [　　　] cm³

(f) 1 L 20 mL = [　　　] cm³

(g) $4\frac{1}{2}$ L = [　　　] cm³

3 A rectangular tank measuring 30 cm by 25 cm by 20 cm is $\frac{3}{4}$ filled with water. Some of the water is then poured into a cubical tank with sides of 15 cm to fill it up. What is the volume of the water in liters and milliliters that is left in the rectangular tank?

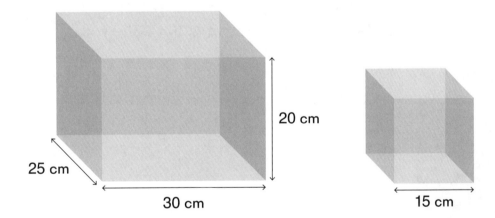

25 cm

30 cm

20 cm

15 cm

4 The container below is filled with water to a depth of 12 cm. What is the volume of water in liters and milliliters?

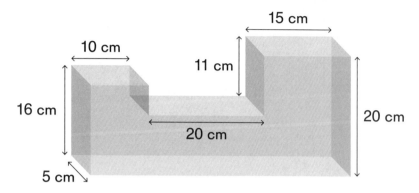

5 A rectangular tank measuring 50 cm by 40 cm by 40 cm is half filled with water. When 4 metal cubes each with an edge of 10 cm are placed in the water, the water level rises. What is the new height of the water?

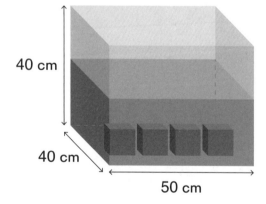

Challenge

6 A solid cube with an edge 30 cm long has 3 square holes with sides 10 cm long cut all the way through to the other side as shown. What is the volume of the remaining solid?

7 A rectangular tank with a base 30 cm by 20 cm is $\frac{1}{2}$ filled with water. After 3 L of water is added to it, it becomes $\frac{3}{5}$ filled with water. What is the height of the water in the tank when it is $\frac{3}{5}$ filled?

Check

1 Use the following number to answer the questions: three hundred ninety-four million, eight hundred one thousand.

(a) Write the number in numerals.

(b) What is the value of the digit 9?

(c) Divide the number by 1,000. What is the new value of the digit 9?

2 Find the values. Express fractions in simplest form.

(a) $21 - 14 \div 7 + 3 \times 9$

(b) $8 - 3 \div 4 + 1 \times 2$

(c) $(2\frac{1}{2} + \frac{2}{3} + 1\frac{5}{6}) \div \frac{1}{5}$

(d) $\frac{1}{2} \times \frac{3}{5} + \frac{1}{4} \div \frac{1}{6}$

3 Ms. Perez earned $6,942 a month for the past 4 years. How much did she earn in all during those 4 years?

4 The area of a rectangle is 1,568 in². One side measures $2\frac{1}{3}$ feet. What is the length of the other side in inches?

5 A bottle can hold 3 L of water. It had $2\frac{1}{2}$ L of water at first and then $\frac{3}{4}$ L was poured out. 785 mL was then added. How many more milliliters of water are needed to fill the bottle?

6 Daniel spent $\frac{1}{3}$ of his money on roller blades and $\frac{1}{6}$ of the remainder on a helmet. He had $155 left. How much money did he have at first?

7 Some bags of rice have a total weight of 30 kg. Each bag of rice weighs $\frac{3}{5}$ kg. How many bags of rice are there?

8 A rectangular city block is twice as long as it is wide. The distance around the block is $\frac{3}{4}$ mile. How wide is the city block?

9 What fraction of the triangle is shaded?

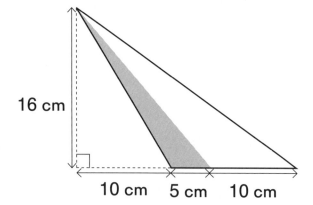

16 cm

10 cm   5 cm   10 cm

10 Find the shaded area in square meters.

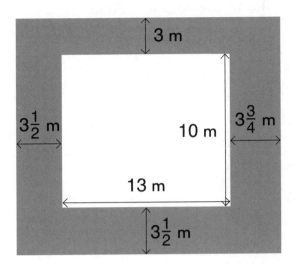

11 Find the area of the following figure.

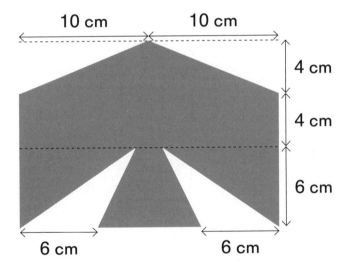

12 A rectangular tank measuring 45 cm by 40 cm by 24 cm was $\frac{1}{2}$ filled with water. When a stone was placed in the tank, the tank became $\frac{3}{4}$ filled.

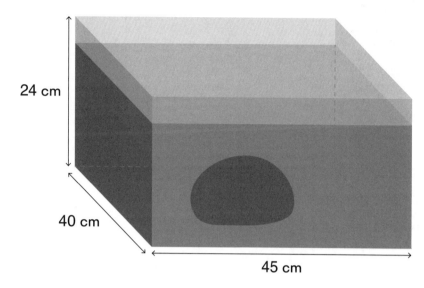

24 cm

40 cm

45 cm

(a) Find the capacity of the tank in liters and milliliters.

(b) Find the volume of the stone.

Challenge

13 The figure shows two identical squares of sides 12 cm overlapping each other. Find the area of the overlapping part.

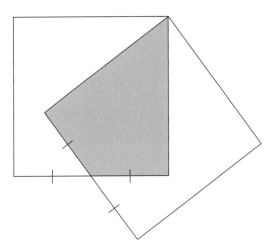

14 A 4-digit multiple of 17 is made up of 4 different digits. What is the least number it could be?

15 How many unit cubes are needed to build each of the following solids?

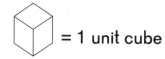 = 1 unit cube

(a)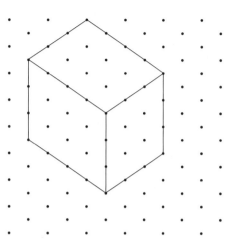

(b)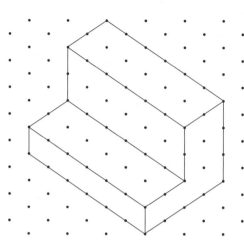

16 Complete the drawing of each cuboid. Then give the volume in cubic units.

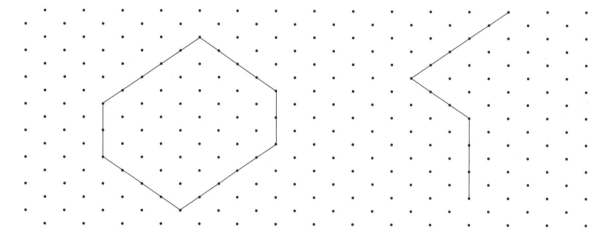

17 Draw a solid figure with a volume of 64 cubic units.